The ETHOS

By Adam J Jackson

THIRDAGE
PUBLISHING

Ethos

The characteristic spirit of a culture, era or community manifested in its attitudes and aspirations.

~

Never doubt that a small group of thoughtful, committed citizens can change the world; indeed, it's the only thing that ever has.

Margaret Mead

Third Age Publishing
An imprint of Bilberry Media Group
1 Coldbath Square, London EC1R 5HL

www.thirdagepublishing.com

First published as The Ethos 2017

A catalogue record for this book is available from the British Library

ISBN 978-1-912424-00-9

Printed and bound in the UK by
CreateSpace

CONTENTS

FICTIONAL DISCLAIMER

The Ethos is inspired by the community at Sun Park Living which is situated in Playa Blanca on the island of Lanzarote. However, this book does not claim to be - nor is it intended to be – an accurate depiction of Sun Park or the people I met there. I have changed the names of the individuals, their physical characteristics, occupations, places of residence and, in some cases, combined elements from several people's experiences into one character. Similarly, whilst some of the dialogue has been drawn from interviews, conversations are mostly my creations. Any resemblance to actual persons, living or dead, or actual events is purely coincidental.

In addition, the Sun Park depicted in *The Ethos* should not be taken to be a true and accurate reflection of the facilities at the actual Sun Park. The resort relaunched its new self-service and self-catering concept in 2012 and it is an evolving project. At the time of writing, there is no Green Kitchen, Cabbage Patch or Learning Annex. However, I am told that these are all planned for the near future.

INTRODUCTION

'If you don't like the way things are, start a village.'
Stephen Brooks

The Ethos was inspired by a small, committed group of people who came together to realise a dream. A community where people enjoy new life adventures, try new activities, experience joy and friendship, and pursue their dreams. Some even rediscover the purpose and meaning of their lives. It is an inclusive community where everyone is welcome, and where nobody need ever feel isolated or alone.

The story began in central London on a typically cold and wet January afternoon. I stepped out of St Paul's underground station and into the freezing, damp air, thankful to be wearing a thick overcoat. It was typical weather for the time of year, overcast, wet, and very cold. Fortunately, my destination was less than a few minutes' walk away.

I was heading to the Royal Exchange to meet an old and very dear friend, Gil Summers. Gil had called me the previous day. We hadn't seen each other for over fifteen years primarily because both of us had moved abroad and were living in different countries. However, we had been in touch intermittently via email and skype. Gil had called to say that he was back in London and we made plans to meet up the following day.

At our meeting, Gil told me about a project he and his partner, Patricia Dominguez, had been working on for the past five years. "Imagine an all year-round summer camp for mature adults." he said. "A place that's safe and secure, where people get to know each other very easily. A place where you're only a few metres away from lots of friends and acquaintances, where you can try new activities, get involved in gardening, ballroom dancing, art, yoga or tai chi...play tennis, learn a new language, go on hikes, cycling trips...whatever takes your fancy. You just turn up and join in."

"An adults-only holiday resort?"

"Except it's not just a resort" he said, "it's a community."

I was intrigued and the following morning I got up at 4:00am and caught the seven o'clock flight from Stansted, London, to Arrecife, Lanzarote, to see this place that Gil had described for myself. I had no idea where my destination was or how long I'd be there. All I knew was that the resort was called 'Sun Park' and it was situated on the south side of the island. Patricia picked me up from the airport and within half an hour I was standing amid palm trees in front of a complex of white-washed buildings.

Walking through the main entrance was like walking into a huge party. There must have been over a hundred people in the main reception, and even more on the main terrace where a saxophonist was playing 'Summertime'. People were milling around, some standing in groups, others sitting around tables and, out on the terrace, a few were dancing. Had I arrived at someone's party? I asked. Patricia smiled. "No. This is Social Friday."

Sun Park is not your typical hotel, it is a secure, private self-service resort dedicated exclusively for adults and, primarily focussed for the fit and active over 50s. On Friday mornings, anyone in the area can pop in to have a look around, and meet the people staying there. It can be daunting arriving at a party where you don't know a soul, but before I could get the keys to my room, a man approached and asked if he could get me a drink. Five minutes later, I was sitting with a crowd of people on the terrace overlooking the swimming pools and gardens. These people are my friends to this day.

I had only intended to stay at Sun Park for the weekend but, I was so taken with the place and the people, I ended up staying for two weeks. By the end of my stay, I had come to understand why Gil had enthused so much about the resort. He and Patricia had created something special. It was a community that, over the years, has touched the lives of thousands of people. They may even have started a revolutionary, new social movement.

People arrive at Sun Park in the belief that they are getting a holiday, or a long winter break, but many leave having had an unexpected, rich and rewarding, life experience. For some, the experience had been so transformational that they have chosen to make Sun Park their second home, and they live there most, and sometimes all, of the year.

I confess that I felt a sense of awe at what had been accomplished at Sun Park. Talking to members of the community, I discovered that Sun Park had changed so many lives. There were a few instances where being at Sun Park saved people's lives.

Both Gil and Patricia are quick to acknowledge that they played only a small part in how Sun Park had evolved. "The heart of everything you see here," Gil told me one evening, "was created by the community." As lovely as the Sun Park resort is, and as beautiful as the surrounding area of Playa Blanca is, the thing that draws people back year after year is the community and their ethos.

Almost without exception, everyone I met at Sun Park who either lived there or was a returning guest, said that the reason they came back to Sun Park was for the ethos. Few could articulate what the ethos was, they just felt a deep sense of belonging, a community spirit that had been missing from many of their lives.

At Sun Park, they had found acceptance, trust and friendship. Discovering how individual and collective responsibility are often one and the same, they had experienced a generosity of spirit that is seldom found today. I became fascinated by the ethos; what were the key elements, and how had it evolved? How had the ethos impacted people's lives? And what could we learn from it?

The ethos had been inspired by a shared vision to create a platform for people who had reached a stage in their lives when many felt lost. Their children may have left home, their careers may have ended, or they may simply be facing an uncertain future. It became apparent that Sun Park was much more than a holiday resort for the over-fifties. I believe that it is a blueprint for something bigger, it may be the start of a social movement that invites us to reconsider our place in the world.

My intention in writing this book is not to give an accurate representation of Sun Park. As with all ventures in life, Sun Park is an evolving project. I must also state for the record that, whilst this book is inspired by the community at Sun Park, the characters are not representations of the people I met. Not only have names and physical characteristics been changed, but I have put words in their mouths that they may not have uttered and, at times, used artistic license with their stories.

In some cases, I have used composite characters, blending several people's accounts into a single character. Therefore, whilst some people reading this book might think they recognise parts of themselves or others, none of the characters or their stories should be taken to be true of any one person. That said, I have tried to be true to the community spirit, the ethos.

My hope is that this book may spread some of the magic that I experienced at Sun Park because the ethos is not confined to one resort situated on a tiny island in the Atlantic Ocean. Ultimately, the ethos is a belief that all we really need to live a long and happy life is friendship, love and a sense of purpose and belonging. With these, regardless of age or ability, every day is a new adventure.

Adam J Jackson
Hertfordshire
July 2017

PROLOGUE

'Just living is not enough...
one must have sunshine, freedom, and a little flower.'
Hans Christian Andersen

Today is the happiest day of my life. It is also the saddest. I know there will never be a day for me quite like this one again. I'm surrounded by my family, I call them family even though we're not related by blood. We have been part of one another's lives, some for many years. We have laughed together, and cried together, and looked out for one another. But our bond is the result of much more than a shared history.

Greg is here. He is a large, burly man with a shaved head. He reminds me of a brown bear with thick set, dark brown eyes framed with large, full crescent eyebrows. At first sight, Greg might appear to some as intimidating but, within minutes of meeting him, you are aware that he has a gentle and generous soul. For as long as I have known him he has greeted everyone he meets, even strangers, not with a formal handshake, but with a hug. His large arms envelope the recipient like a goose-down duvet exuding genuine affection.

Greg is a rare breed; a philosopher, but also a pragmatist. A successful entrepreneur and businessman who, together with his partner, Christina, is responsible for laying the foundations of where I am today. Without them, without everyone here today, I know beyond a shadow of a doubt that my life would have turned out very differently.

Of course, Christina is here too. She is a good foot shorter than Greg with shoulder length auburn hair, and matching brown eyes which are a shade lighter than Greg's. Like Greg, Christina has kind soul. She genuinely cares about everyone who is part of the community. The project that she and Greg started many years ago was inspired as much by her, and her family and her background, as it was by Greg's. It was many years ago that Greg and Christina had a shared vision, a dream that started with a handful of people and went on to inspire and change the lives of thousands all over the world, including my own.

Greg has a wonderful mantra, it is one that has had a profound and lasting impact on me. It is a mantra which, since hearing it, I have tried to live my life by. I must admit that the first time he said it, I found it irritating. A flight that I was booked on the following week had been cancelled. I was frustrated and angry. How was I to get home? Greg put his arm around my shoulder, and softly said, 'Stan, you're here now, and that's all that matters.'

Of course, it all turned out fine, as most things tend to do. The flight got re-scheduled and I got home safely, albeit a day later than planned. Nobody died. There had been no tragedy. I hadn't been hurt or harmed in any way. As Mark Twain had observed, we spend most of our lives worrying about things that never happen. 'Worry' he remarked, 'was a debt that we don't yet owe.'

Had I not listened to Greg, I would have remained anxious and fretted, perhaps for days. I would have wasted time and energy worrying about something over which I had no control. At my age, time is a very precious commodity.

I soon understood the wisdom in Greg's mantra. There have been too many times in my life when I have sacrificed time to worry about things that may or may not happen in the future, rather than just focusing on the present, the here and now. Today, of all days, the mantra has special significance. Greg doesn't have to remind me. I hear his words echo in my head. 'You're here now. And that's all that matters!'.

It is a magnificent day, although most days here are just as lovely. The sun is shining in a clear, blue sky. There isn't a single cloud to be seen. The gardens are resplendent, both in colour and aroma. To me, this is paradise. I close my eyes and breathe in the rich, plant fragrances - lavender, mint, and beautiful Jasmine that always brings back memories of my honeymoon over three decades earlier in Cyprus.

I close my eyes to take in the sounds. I can hear the tropical birds in the trees. Barney, a former professional musician who retired over a decade ago, is here and playing 'My Way' on his saxophone. Even sweeter is the sound of the people. Lots of people, talking and laughing. It's a party, after all. A perfect day. We are all here, together, and right at this moment, that really is all that matters.

Of course, I am aware that very soon I must leave. I have come to love this place. It has become my home just as the people have become my family. Yet, very soon I will be saying farewell. I know that I may never return, but I will take this place with me. I will take the people with me, in my heart. How could I not? We have a common bond. It comes from the ethos, the spirit that runs through the entire community.

Many times, people have asked me what makes this place so special, and the answer has always been the same; it is the ethos. Everyone here will tell you the same thing. They enjoy the sunshine and the beach, and they love this island; but the reason they return, year after year, the reason some have chosen to make it their second home, and the reason that this place is so wonderful, and so unique, is the ethos.

Some say that to really understand the ethos, you need to experience it. It's a bit like my late wife's carrot cake; I can list the ingredients and explain the recipe; I can try to describe the soft, moist texture laced with tiny flecks of ginger and coconut, filled with generous layers of orange cream, and topped with walnut pieces. But, any attempt I could make to convey the taste of that cake would inevitably fail because, until you have a piece of that cake on a plate in front of you, and until you slice through it with a fork, and put it into your mouth, and experience it melting like butter on your tongue, you'll never be able to truly appreciate that cake.

I know that I have been lucky, or blessed, call it what you will. My life could have worked out very differently. There was a time, not so long ago when, to all intents and purposes, my life was over. The reason it didn't end I can only put down to the ethos, and that is why I am sharing my story.

My hope is my story will give you a glimpse into what the ethos is, and why it can make a difference to your life as it has for mine and hundreds, if not thousands, of other people. Whether I succeed or not, only you can judge.

Stanley Davis
St Albans
Hertfordshire

CHAPTER 1: LOST OPPORTUNITIES

'Lost opportunities, lost possibilities, feelings we can never get back. That's part of what it means to be alive.'
Haruki Murakami (Kafka on the Shore)

Twenty-seven years earlier...

Have you ever felt that your life has been wasted? I've felt it many times over the years. Every now and again the feeling has engulfed me, suffocated me. I feel it now on my sixtieth birthday. That's a big number. At least, it is to me. Especially today.

"You're well old" my lovely daughter likes to tease me. There is no irony when I say 'lovely'. Sabrina really is lovely. She's 28 years old, very beautiful, like her mother. You may think I'm a bit biased, and I am. I'm her father, after all. But, you won't find a single person who knows Sabrina who would disagree with me. She lives in North London, about a forty-minute drive from my home in St Albans, Hertfordshire. She runs her own film production company and works ridiculous hours, but she loves what she does.

My son, James, is younger by two and a half years. He isn't married, but is living with Emma, his girlfriend of the past five years. Funnily enough, James is also in the film industry, although he works in animation and special effects. He was relocated to California three years ago by the company who hired him straight out of University.

According to Wikipedia, StreetArtFX is an up and coming 3D animation studio on the cutting edge of new technology in animation and special effects. James tells me that the movie he is working on has been short-listed for this year's Oscars. Should that happen, the sky's the limit, I guess. James says that they've had meetings with Pixar and a takeover may be on the cards. So, these are exciting times for him.

Both of my children seem happy. Sabrina married her childhood sweetheart, Steven Cooper, three years ago and they have two baby girls, Phoebe and Christina. Steven, is a psychologist and has become a second son. He is a caring, thoughtful man and, most importantly, like James and I, Steven is a lifelong Manchester United fan.

I speak to them both regularly - at least once a week - although I see them far less often. I don't blame them for that. They both lead busy lives. Sabrina skyped me this morning and she and the children sang Happy Birthday. She's a good girl. James is a little less frequent with his calls, but boys are different, aren't they? To be fair to him, he did send me a message on Facebook.

I'm proud of my children, and I love them both to bits, but I have come to accept that they have their own lives. They ask me how I am, and I tell them I'm fine. Which is true. I am fine. Although, if I'm totally honest, fine is no longer enough. The truth is that I have been feeling increasingly lonely the past few years, but I don't want to burden them with my problems. That wouldn't do them - or me - any good.

I don't usually think of myself as a lonely person even though, outside my work, I spend most of my time alone. My wife, Kelly, passed away four years ago. She died suddenly from a heart attack. Life is so fragile. Literally, one minute you can be cooking dinner, listening to the news on TV and the next minute, you feel a sudden tightening around your chest.

I was on my way home from work when it happened. Had I been there - had anyone been there, for that matter - it's possible Kelly would have lived. But, if's and but's and maybes don't matter a jot. All that counts is what is, not what might have been.

Kelly was gone, and her death had left a massive void in my life. We used to do everything together; we'd go on holidays, enjoy bridge evenings with friends, and of course, many evenings we'd just stay in and watch something on TV or read. I think it was when I lost Kelly that my life began to disintegrate. Certainly, my social life did.

My parents passed away many years ago, as did my aunts and uncles on both sides. I have cousins, of course, but I only see them on special occasions like births, weddings - and in more recent times - funerals.

I see my brother Mike and his wife, Leanne, two or three times a month. Mostly, Mike and I watch football together. We're both life-long supporters of Manchester United. Before you ask, we weren't born in or near Manchester. In fact, we came from Brighton which is about as far south in the UK as you can get from Manchester. When we were young, our family moved to Canada and, like millions of other football fans around the world, we fell in love with the Red Devils.

Despite an extended family, children and grandchildren, I still find myself here, by myself, sitting in my kitchen at 9:00pm on the eve of my birthday. Why am I not out celebrating? Well, for starters, I've never been one for big birthday celebrations. Most of my family and friends live too far away and are far too busy for a celebration during the week. Let's face it, Monday is not everybody's favourite evening for a night out. Truth be told, even if it were a Friday night, I don't think I'd feel like celebrating. Aside from turning sixty, something happened to me today that ruined any chance of celebration; I was made redundant.

I have worked in the same job for the same company for the past twenty-eight years. I am a credit finance officer for a large, American car manufacturer. I can't say that I was surprised at losing my job. The car market is cut-throat competitive, and our market share has been shrinking by the year. I'm not the only one who lost their job either. My problem, being sixty years of age, is that I really don't know where it leaves me, or my place in the world.

I'm not sorry to leave the job. I certainly won't miss it. About ten years ago, the company brought in 'open' office plans with 'hot desks'. It sounded like a good idea. Nobody has claim to a desk. You arrive and sit down at whatever desk is available in your department. Next to a window is prime real estate but, wherever you sit, you're still boxed into a two-square metre cubicle with panels to the front and either side. Once you've sat down in your 'cube', you don't see anyone or anything.

I can't believe I stuck with the job for so long. I could have left years ago. I could've taken a risk, looked for another job. I could've tried to do something for myself. Start my own business. Why didn't I? Fear. Fear of loss, fear of the unknown. Plus, I had a pension to consider, although that didn't work out the way I had hoped. Like most people, I didn't foresee the financial crash, and then I had to come to terms with the fact that, overnight, the value of my pension fund was cut by sixty percent.

Would it have made much difference if I had sought a different job? Wouldn't I have just ended up in another cubicle? Probably. I can't say for sure because I never tried. Perhaps I stayed put because I had lost some self-confidence. It doesn't boost your self-esteem when you have a boss who is an illiterate moron called Sheldon, less than half your age and who has never read a book that didn't have pictures in it!

If I sound slightly bitter about work and, particularly about Sheldon, that's because I am. Four thirty this afternoon, he called me into his office. Sheldon and upper management don't work in cubicles like the rest of us. Without any preamble, he said that he was sorry but, due to 'corporate restructuring', they would have to 'let me go'. You hear those words a lot in TV dramas and movies. The boss fires the underling and tries to insinuate that it is the underling's choice to leave.

I don't know what my future holds. What is a man of my age supposed to do? What can I do? Suddenly everything seems uncertain which is why I'm sitting alone in my kitchen, drinking a cheap bottle of rioja. If alcohol is supposed to numb the anxiety, it isn't working. My head is pounding, my lower back is aching and, I could be imagining it but my skin seems to be itching more than usual. I've suffered with a skin condition called psoriasis my entire life. It comes and goes. I look down at my wrist and I see that, without realising it, I've scratched to the point of bleeding. The same thought overwhelms me; what I'm going to do for the rest of my life?

I know that the best years have gone and, if I am honest, other than my children and grandchildren, I've got very little to show for it. My pension, such that it is, doesn't kick in for another seven years, maybe more. I saw on the news last week that the retirement age is going to be raised beyond seventy. That means I'm going to have to find another job. I may have to sell my home. Thankfully, despite the recent financial crash, I have equity in my house although, with the current slump in the property market, it wouldn't be anywhere near enough to support me for the rest of my life.

Travelling home on the train this evening, I became immersed in feelings of disillusionment, bordering on despair. By some fluke, I managed to get a window seat. It was already dark outside, and raining heavily. A scene from the movie, 'The Bucket List' came to my mind. Morgan Freeman and Jack Nicholson play two men diagnosed with terminal illnesses who decide to write their 'bucket lists' - things they want to do and the places they want to visit before their time is up. In the scene, as the two men stand overlooking the Pyramids of Giza in Egypt, Morgan Freeman recalls an ancient Egyptian belief about death. 'When a soul arrives at the entrance to heaven, it is greeted by guards who ask just two questions, the answers to which determine whether the soul is allowed to enter or not: Have you found joy in your life? And have you brought joy to others?'

If a life is judged by the joy it has given or received, then I'd give mine a D minus, maybe a C. What a shame it is that we don't have a teacher to continue to coach and mentor us in adulthood, marking our progress. 'Must try harder', 'Is not fulfilling his potential' or 'Could do so much better!'. Would having someone there beside us push us to do more? To become more? Is that why so many people turn to Life Coaches these days? I really don't know. All I do know is that I have drifted through most, if not all, of my adult life.

I never pursued a dream or had a plan, other than to make a living, but making a living and making a life don't always mean the same thing. Right at this moment, outside of my immediate family, I can't say that I've known much of joy, given or received.

Looking out of the rain-splattered window on the train in to the darkness, it occurred to me that so many people, like me, spend their lives in their own self-imposed cubicles. There may be no carpeted panels, but the feeling of isolation is just as real. I noticed people all around me on the train fixated on their smartphones or iPads, completely oblivious to everyone and everything going on around them. It seems that these days people prefer to live in a digital world, a virtual reality. Real life gets pushed to one side until it fades into nothingness. Even those who were travelling together were mesmerised by the virtual world on their hand-held devices rather than engaging in the real world with their companions.

Today they trap you young. Apparently, more infants under the age of five use an iPad than can tie their shoelaces! That might be due to the advent of Velcro, or it could be that children are just as addicted to their electronic devices as adults. Recently, I read that children in the UK typically spend less than an hour a day playing outside. That's less time than most hardened criminals get to be outside, in the open air!

One day, when these children become adults, they'll look up from their screens and, like me, wonder what they did with their lives. Where did the time go? Who'd have thought that a 4cm x 9cm LED screen would lock you in a cubicle away from the rest of the world?

I don't mean to be judgemental. I am as guilty as the next person, but today is the first time I've really noticed how disconnected from people I've become. That's why I am sitting here, on my birthday, alone. And, that's probably also why I've decided to go on a holiday tomorrow...on my own.

I saw adverts in the evening paper which made me think, 'Sod it. Why not get away for a week in the sun?'. It's 7th January, it's freezing cold outside. It gets dark by the middle of the afternoon, and it's been raining non-stop for most of the past week. On two occasions, it was so cold that the rain turned to hail. If I stay here, I'll only be moping around the house, not to mention the fact that I haven't had a proper holiday since Kelly passed away.

So, I'm off in the morning. Hopefully, the break might do me some good. Somewhere with sunshine, of course. Hopefully, at the very least, it will do my skin some good. Psoriasis tends to get better in sunshine.

I haven't seen real sunshine, the kind in which you can just sit out and feel the warmth on your skin, for a very long time. Last year's summer was a total washout, typical here in the UK. The winters are cold and damp too. Recently I've been getting to work before the sun has risen and, by the time I leave the office, the sun has already set. Scientists say that there's insufficient daylight in our winter months for our bodies to manufacture adequate amounts of vitamin D. They've given it an apt name - SAD - Seasonal Affective Disorder. Perhaps that's why I feel so miserable? It doesn't take a doctor to tell you that living in the cold and dark isn't the best environment for one's physical or mental health to thrive.

As soon as I got home this evening I googled 'destinations for winter sun'. The Telegraph website was first to appear with an article entitled 'Winter destinations with guaranteed sunshine'. The list began: Barbados, Dubai, Cape Town, Miami... all of which are a bit too far, or too expensive, for my budget. Then the Canary Islands appeared.

I checked the world map. The Canaries are Spanish islands situated just off the north-west coast of Africa. They enjoy a warm, temperate climate all year round, and the forecast for the coming week was showing 18 - 23 degrees with blue skies all the way. Perfect!

After much deliberation, I chose a resort on Lanzarote, the fourth-largest and easternmost island. The Cayman Beach Hotel in Playa Blanca. It is only a 3-star rating, but the pictures looked nice enough, and it was only a short walk to the beach. Prices were reasonable, and even though it was last minute, Ryanair had a return flight for less than the cost of a return journey by train to Manchester.

If everything goes according to plan, tomorrow morning I'll be on the 7:35am flight from London Stansted Airport to Lanzarote for a week in the sun. I know this isn't the answer to my problems. To be perfectly honest, I don't know if I'm doing the right thing but, it will give me the chance to get away, if only for a week. I'm hoping that I'll be able to clear my head, to think, to breathe, to feel the sun on my skin. For now, that may have to be enough. I guess I'll have plenty of time to worry about what I'm going to do with the rest of my life when I get back.

CHAPTER 2: TIME ALONE

*'I think it's good for a person to spend time alone.
It gives them an opportunity to discover who they are,
and to figure out why they are always alone.'*
Amy Sedaris

I'm used to getting up early. My alarm has gone off at 6:15am every weekday for the past thirty-five years. That gives me just enough time for a shower, shave and a cup of coffee before leaving the house at 7:00am for work.

It takes about half an hour for me to drive to Borehamwood and Elstree station and, on good days, I'd arrive in time to catch the 7:38 fast train to Farringdon. From there, it's a ten-minute walk to the office so I'd usually be sitting at my desk by 8:30.

Today my alarms went off at 4:15am. I say alarms because I set two - one on my phone and the other on my iPad, just in case. As it turned out, I didn't need either. I had woken hourly through the night, such was my anxiety at the prospect of oversleeping and missing the flight. The taxi arrived on time and I was at the airport exactly two hours before the flight was due to depart.

I can't say the flight was enjoyable. What budget airlines are these days? But, it wasn't too uncomfortable for a four-hour flight. I sat in a window seat, which is my preference. I can see the attraction of aisle seats, they give you the freedom to get out of your seat whenever you like, and you can disembark faster from an aisle seat too. But, given a choice, I'll take the window seat every time. It always fascinates me how you can be looking out at a grey, overcast scene - it might even be pouring with rain - and then, within a matter of seconds, you're in bright sunshine looking at clear blue skies above a canopy of white, fluffy clouds below. It's like being transported to another world.

I don't fly frequently enough to take those views from 30,000 feet for granted. There is a lot that I have taken for granted though. I travelled on the same train to work and back for the best part of three decades but, right at this moment, I couldn't tell you what you would see from the window of that train. To be fair, there weren't many times when I could get a seat on the train, never mind a seat by the window. But, there were times when I was able to look out of the window, I just never really paid much attention.

The same could be said of my journey through life, I suppose. I've travelled some distance, but I can't recall many of the scenes. Honestly, sitting here, I couldn't tell you where the years have gone. I've taken a lot for granted, I know I have. I was always so focussed on the usual stresses of daily living. It's always been about work and paying the bills, and keeping my head above water to the exclusion of everything else that may have been going on around me.

~

The first thing you notice as you step out of the plane at Arrecife airport is the bright, vivid colours. Coming from the grey, winter skies back in England, it feels as if you are stepping into a new technicolour world. Then you feel the warmth of the sunshine on your face tempered by a cool, ocean breeze. According to the guide books, the temperature is pretty much constant throughout the year. Mostly, it stays around 20 - 25 in the day, and it rarely strays beyond 30 degrees at the top and 12 at the bottom. I wondered to myself why I'd never been here before? With low levels of humidity, this is very possibly the perfect climate.

Lanzarote was born out of fiery eruptions, it hosts over 300 active volcanoes. In 1730, a volcano on the west of the island known as 'Timanfaya' erupted causing all life on the island to be swallowed by a river of molten lava. The landscape turned into a barren, dark carpet of black and brown rock which formed over the following decades as the lava settled. However, there is a flipside to the virtual obliteration of animal and plant life; lava brings with it gifts. For the land, at least. The hard-set rock formed out of the lava is packed with minerals. It also helps the soil retain moisture, and it provides a protective cover from the sun and wind. On an island set in the Atlantic Ocean that sees less than thirteen centimetres of rain a year, these benefits can't be over-emphasised.

Once over the mountain, heading south, several coastal towns come into view. One of them is Playa Blanca, a charming fishing village characterised with low-level white washed buildings, and streets lined with palm trees. The town is framed by a sea that sparkles as if covered with diamonds resting under a clear, blue sky.

The hotel is a large complex of studio apartments surrounding tropical gardens and there are numerous swimming pools and play areas. I was shown to my apartment which was on the ground floor: a double bedroom, a bathroom, a small living room with a kitchenette, and patio doors leading out to a small terrace.

You wouldn't call the accommodation five-star luxury. The furniture looks like it has seen better days, and the walls could do with a lick of paint but, to be fair, it is clean, and it is surprisingly spacious. I am grateful to be here and very happy that this will be my home for the next six days.

~

Playa Blanca is surprisingly beautiful. It's flat, and very easy to get around on foot. The beach is only a ten-minute walk from my hotel and, once there, a paved promenade extends for miles and miles in both directions. To the West a five-minute walk leads to the old town, a bustling centre of shops and restaurants. Past the old town is the port. Small fishing boats depart each morning and passenger ferries go back and forth to the neighbouring island of Fuerteventura. To the East is the marina which looks to be a more prosperous, upmarket enclave of modern white washed buildings - apartments, hotels, shops and restaurants - all overlooking hundreds of yachts and motor boats.

The coastline is breath-taking, whichever way you go. I walked for miles in both directions. I don't remember ever having walked so far in my life. Then again, walking in the cold, wet weather back home just isn't the same. At Playa Blanca, the air is warm but not humid, and you can almost taste the marine ozone in the air and feel the oxygen fill your lungs as it blows in from the Atlantic Ocean.

It may be all in my imagination, but I feel more alive here. To think, only last week I was walking to my cube from Farringdon station in London. There the air is so heavy and rank with diesel and petrol fumes that cyclists - and even some pedestrians - use masks covering their mouths and noses to filter the toxic particles. I never wore a mask. Perhaps I should have. Sometimes the air in London is so bad that warnings for asthmatics and the elderly are issued on the radio and TV news. I'm not having a pop at London. Many other big cities around the world are far, far worse. But, here on Lanzarote, just 75 miles off the coast of North Africa, the air is as clean and pure as the azure, blue sea.

As I headed back to the hotel from the beach, I walked a little further along the front. Not far. Perhaps a few hundred metres. Instead of turning back, I took a parallel path and ended up at a crossroads. The five-star Princess Yaiza hotel to my left and a small *supermercado* to my right. The prices of food and drink are very reasonable compared with those I pay back home, which is remarkable when you consider that Lanzarote is such a small island. I stopped to buy some water and fruit juice, a bag of mixed nuts, and a bottle of *Gran Reserva Vino Tinto* to take back to my apartment.

It had been a beautiful afternoon and I felt pleased with myself for choosing this island, and especially Playa Blanca. In truth, the choice had hardly been deliberate. I could just as easily have ended up on one of the neighbouring islands. Tenerife and Fuerteventura had both been options, and I'd also considered going to Morocco.

Lost in my thoughts, I found myself walking past a resort on my left. A stretch of low rise white buildings lined with palm trees, not too dissimilar to the resort where I was staying. It wasn't the resort itself that made me stop and cross the road to take a closer look. It was the large, colourful posters - five in total - either side of the entrance.

Sun Park Village: A Holiday-Living Resort for Active Over-50s. It went on to explain that it represented a 'revolutionary new approach to life after full-time employment.' I was particularly drawn to the penultimate paragraph on the second poster:

'Sun Park Village welcomes anyone who is looking for a fresh start; a chance to explore new interests and activities, to meet new people, and to share their life's experience with other liked-minded people.'

The words on the posters resonated in me, not just because of the situation I had left back home. Yes, I had lost my job but, more importantly, I had come to the realization that I had neglected so much in my life. The words 'explore', 'new activities' with 'new people' were no longer in my everyday vocabulary. Surely, it would be foolish, at my time of life, to even entertain any ideas of a 'fresh start'? I know that, for me, it is unthinkable. The best years have been and gone. I could have done more...I should have done more. And yet, I couldn't help but wonder, what if these posters were right? What if a fresh start was possible?

The posters piqued my interest, and I was determined to find out more. I pushed against the large double-fronted glass doors, but they wouldn't budge. Peering through, I could see there were people inside. To the far left were five tables, each with four people sat playing cards. Beyond them, further to the left, were a handful of people sitting in a lounge area. I could see other people sitting on a terrace beyond. I knocked, but they were some distance inside and there was another set of double doors between me and them. They couldn't hear me.

Unable to attract anyone's attention, I went back to re-read the posters. Only then did I fully appreciated why the doors were closed to the public. This was not a standard holiday resort in the traditional sense; it was a private, gated community. But whilst people could not simply walk in off the street, there was a way to look inside and even meet some of the people. It was mentioned on the final poster; The heading read: 'Social Friday'.

CHAPTER 3: SOCIAL FRIDAY

'Opportunities are like sunrises. If you wait too long,
you miss them.'
William Arthur Ward

Friday is the day I looked forward to most throughout my adult life. I would awake in the morning just that little bit happier in the knowledge that the end of the working day would mark the beginning of two days of freedom. 'Thank God It's Friday', the restaurant chain built their whole brand around people's desire to reach the weekend. Ribs, burgers and beer on a Friday night out. Two days when a person's time was their own and The Cube could be forgotten.

I awoke to a very different feeling on my first Friday in Playa Blanca. Excitement might not be the right word. It was more... curiosity. I was curious to find out what an adults-only holiday-living community was all about.

The previous evening, I googled the resort on my smartphone. It looked very much like the hotel I was staying in, two large pools and gardens surrounded by very similar two storey apartments. The Wi-Fi connection in my hotel wasn't strong enough for me to watch any videos, but I was able to access all the other content. I reviewed the Picture Gallery and the About Us page, and read through a list of glowing endorsements on the Testimonial page. It sounded exciting, and I was eager to see it for myself.

I ate breakfast alone for the fifth time that week, washed and read the paper. At 10:15am, I was standing outside the gates of Sun Park Village. The front doors were open, and I could see quite a crowd of people gathered inside the main foyer. As I walked through, to my left was what looked like a hotel reception area. In the middle of the room was a rectangular glass atrium surrounded by an assortment of tropical plants. To the far right was a small cafe, and straight ahead two sets of double glass doors lead out onto a terrace.

A crowd of perhaps twenty people were sitting around three tables playing ukuleles and singing *You Are My Sunshine*. To my right, in front of the cafe, more people had gathered, some standing, some sitting, all holding drinks and chatting. As I approached, a man wearing an Australian outback hat - without the corks - walked up to me smiling. 'Hello' he said, offering his hand.

'Hi' I replied, shaking his hand.

"My name is Jacob," he said, with an accent I couldn't quite place.

"Hi Jacob. I'm Stan."

"Welcome to Sun Park, Stan. Can I get you a drink? Tea? Coffee? Juice? Maybe a smoothie? What would you like?"

I opted for a coffee. Jacob handed me a cup and led me through to the terrace.

There must have been around a hundred people, some standing, talking in small groups, and others sitting on chairs around tables and on wicker garden furniture situated under large parasols. The terrace covered a large area, perhaps a hundred square metres, and overlooked lush, tropical gardens. In the middle of the gardens were two large curved pools, one slightly higher than the other, and sunbeds were dotted around. The gardens and pool areas were overlooked by two storey white washed apartments. Beyond the buildings, all that could be seen were mountains in the distance and the azure, blue sky.

Jacob led me to the far end of the terrace, introducing me to some of the people we passed along the way.

"It looks like it's come straight out of a picture postcard." I said, looking at the gardens.

"Thank you." Jacob said. He led me to a group of five people, two men and three women, sitting around a table. "This is Stan", Jacob said, putting his arm on my shoulder. "He's visiting from the UK." Jacob introduced me to them all in turn.

"Will you excuse me?" said Jacob and he headed back into the reception.

"Take a seat," said George, a tall angular man, well-groomed with a full head of white hair, bright blue eyes and, like most of the people there, a tanned complexion. He was wearing light blue shorts and a white tee shirt.

Everyone in the group was staying at Sun Park. George and his wife had been coming for the previous four years. "The first time we came was shortly after it opened," George said. "The pool wasn't in use; the gardens were overgrown..."

"And you still wanted to come back?" I said.

"Yes," he replied laughing. "The pools were repaired and look at them now!"

The two circular pools were a bright aqua, the water crystal clear. "But we don't come for the swimming pools or the gardens. We come here because it has something you won't find anywhere else...a unique ethos."

"The ethos?" I said.

"The community spirit." George said. "Honestly, where would you prefer to be – in a standard hotel sitting for days or weeks by yourself, or in a place like this where you can be participating in any number of activities and always have people around to talk to?"

"That's a bit of a no-brainer." I said. I'd enjoyed my time on the island, but I'd spent most of the week alone. I like spending some time alone, but being alone has its limits. There is no question that had I been able to join in group activities with like-minded people I would have had a completely different experience.

"The problems with the pool and the gardens didn't bother us one bit." George continued. "I mean, the pool is great now, but the beach isn't even a five-minute walk down the road.

"As far as the gardens are concerned, a group of us decided to spend a morning clearing them. It was actually a lot of fun. So much so that now the members and guests continued to look after the gardens."

"Hold on," I said, thinking that I may have misunderstood what George had just said. "Are you saying that the guests here do all of the gardening? Are there no gardening staff at all?"

George smiled. "That's exactly what I'm saying. The only full-time staff on the resort are Miguel, who is in charge of all maintenance and utilities, and his assistant, Paco."

I was dumbfounded. A resort with 220 apartments had only two full-time staff?

Tony, a small man from Wales, chipped in. "The thing is, Sun Park is more of a community than a hotel."

"Yes, but how does that work?"

"It kind of evolved," said George. "Those guests who enjoyed gardening started to look after the gardens, the artists among us did the murals and set up the art studio, other people ran classes – yoga, Pilates, photography."

"So, everyone does something?"

"No." said Tony. "There is no obligation whatsoever for anyone to do anything. It's up to you. If you want to get involved in any of the projects you can, and if you don't, that's fine too."

"Yes," said George. "It's your time and you spend it however you choose. Naturally, people who come on a short stay will want to rest and get out and see the island. But, those who stay for longer – and a lot of people stay for months or even years – enjoy contributing. Today, pretty much everything is organised by members of the community."

I turned to the women in the group. "What do you think?"

Carole, a spinster and retired nurse from Somerset, said that she wasn't a gardener but she organised needlework classes. Gloria, her friend, was recently widowed and just wanted to be among friends. Sun Park, she said, was her sanctuary. She was booked to stay for six months and, from time-to-time, helped in the laundry. "It's not a big thing," she said. "Most people do their own laundry. It's self-service, after all, but some people want or need their laundry done for them."

"I've never come across anything like what you're describing." I said.

"Neither had we." Said Tony, "that's what makes this place so special."

It turned out that I had a lot in common with some of the group. George's daughter lived in the neighbouring village to mine. Tony used to work in the same building as my former office, he lived in West Hampstead and used to get on the same train I took going to work. Carole had worked in Watford General Hospital which is where both of my children were born. When you start talking to people it is astonishing to discover the things that connect us.

We continued chatting for ten or fifteen minutes before Jacob returned. "This is Pippa," he said introducing me to the woman on his right. She was a slim woman with short, layered hair that covered her ears. "Pippa's been here since we opened. She was just about to show some people around and I thought you might like a quick tour."

"Sure. That'd be great." I said.

~

Pippa showed me and another couple around the resort. The complex was made up of two large quadrangles. The first had two large circular swimming pools surrounded by gardens which were overlooked by the main terrace. The second quadrant had a large oval pool, very similar in style, also surrounded by lush tropical gardens, but with the addition of an open-air bar area with seating for perhaps eighty or so people. Past the bar were layered patios, each perhaps twenty-five square meters in size, and to the right a Pétanque court. Pippa explained that this section was where members did outdoor activities including Tai Chi, Meditation, Yoga and, of course, Boules, or Pétanque as the French call it.

"How much do the activities cost?" I asked.

"Most of the activities are free." she said, smiling.

"Free?"

"Yes. That's because many activities are organised by members of the community. Of course, there are paid activities available too. You can take professional classes, workshops, seminars, that sort of thing. But, every day there are community-led activities which are available to everyone completely free of charge."

Pippa led me down a set of stairs to a lower level. There she showed me a fully equipped gym, an art studio, a community shop which was much like a small corner shop you find in the UK selling a range of essential food and pharmacy items. Right at the end was a large hall with a stage, tables and chairs and a drinks bar that stretched across the far end of the room.

"My goodness!" I exclaimed. "This is huge".

Pippa smiled. "This is the Marigold bar. It's open 24 hours a day. You'll find people in here most evenings. There's always something going on down here; during the day, there are activities like Pilates, Yoga, music… that sort of thing. In the evenings, it's used as a communal lounge and there are dance classes, shows, quizzes that are run from here too."

Pippa was obviously very proud of facilities. Everything in the room including the paint on the walls had been supplied or created by the community. All I could say was "Amazing!".

"Would you like to see what the apartments are like?"

"Sure. Lead the way." I said. I'd seen pictures in the local magazine and on the internet but we all know how those can be manipulated and touched up with Photoshop, so I was genuinely interested to see what the apartments were really like.

Pippa took me to her own apartment which was on the ground floor of the East quadrangle. As we walked along the path, it was clear that each ground floor apartment had its own terrace and small garden whereas the first-floor apartments each had their own balcony. Pippa's garden was neat and colourful. There was a row of small Lavender bushes fronted by mini cacti and aloe vera, and white jasmine was growing up the side wall.

"I look after my little garden patch", Pippa said. "I have a thing for Lavender, it reminds me of my honeymoon in Provence. I added the Aloe because it needs little tending and the gel is wonderful for sunburn."

Pippa showed me inside her apartment and explained that, although the other apartments were identical, some people who chose to stay at Sun Park for months or, in some cases, years, added their own furniture and knick-knacks.

Pippa was one of a small but growing group of members who had made Sun Park their second home. Her apartment certainly looked more like a home than a holiday let. Watercolour paintings hung on the walls, mostly flower arrangements which were not to my taste, but then each to their own. That said, Pippa's apartment looked very comfortable and had a homely feel to it. It was certainly a far cry from the hotel room I was staying in.

We walked back to join the others on the main terrace.

"So, what do you think?" asked George.

"I have to say I'm very impressed, George." I said. "To be honest, it almost seems too good to be true."

They all laughed.

"What?" I asked, feeling my cheeks redden.

"Everyone says that!" said George.

"Greg!" Jacob called to a large, burly man with a shaved head and thick set dark brown eyes who was passing. He gave the customary Spanish two kiss greeting to the two women at our table and, George and Tony, a warm handshake. Then he turned to me. "Hi. Welcome to Sun Park. I'm Greg." he said extending his hand.

"Hi Greg. Pleased to meet you, I'm Stan. How long have you been coming here for?"

"I've been here since it opened." he said with a wide smile.

The others smiled too. George interjected, "None of us would be here without Greg."

"Really? Why is that?" I asked.

"Greg is one of the founders." said Pippa.

"Ah! So, this is all your creation?" I said, turning to Greg.

"Absolutely not!" he said, pulling up a chair to join us.

"Everything you see was created by the people who come and stay here. I can't take credit for their achievements."

"You're too modest." said George.

"Not at all." insisted Greg. "Yes, my partner Christina and I laid the foundations, but everything that you see here today...it all comes down to the community.

~

Greg explained that Sun Park had originally been an all-inclusive family holiday resort. I'd taken my family on a quite a few all-inclusive holidays when the children were young. The great thing about them was that you knew exactly how much you'd be spending down to the last penny because all the food and drink was included in the cost of the holiday. The downside is that you tend not to venture out as much and explore the local cafes and restaurants.

"One of the reasons the all-inclusive model doesn't work well here in Playa Blanca," Greg said, "is that there are so many diverse, local restaurants, and the prices are very reasonable."

"I noticed that." I said.

"We weren't interested in building a business around family holidays." Greg explained. "We were more interested offering a new experience for mature adults based upon an ethos of inclusivity, friendship, a sense of camaraderie, in a safe, welcoming environment. This is more than a holiday experience, it is a life experience.

"There is one fundamental flaw with Western society today." continued Greg. "Millions of people have finished raising their families, they've come to the end of their careers, and they're largely forgotten. Many don't get to see their children more than once a week, if they're lucky, because their children are too busy with their own lives. Often, they're left sitting alone, feeling isolated in their homes. It's not good!"

I nodded. These were all things that I had been mulling over the past week.

"On top of loneliness and feelings of isolation", said Greg, "there is the question of just being."

"I don't follow?" I said.

"There is a saying", said Greg, "that many people die in their fifties, only to be buried in their eighties. They reach a point when they stop looking forward, they believe their time has passed. They see a downward spiral of increasing health problems, fewer friends, and declining physical ability. But, we believe - no, we know - that it doesn't have to be that way. It's possible to live in good health, and find fulfilment and happiness, at any stage of life.

"Our vision is simple; we want to encourage people to continue to dream, to rediscover their life's purpose, whatever their age. We believe that the third stage of life - life beyond raising a family and pursuing a career - can be as joyful and happy and rewarding as any of the preceding stages of our lives."

Greg had an almost mesmeric aura. His voice had a light, friendly tone, but what I found compelling was the genuine enthusiasm he had for what he was saying. I could feel the hairs on my arms rise. Could it really be possible that someone my age, at my time of life, could 'rediscover his life's purpose'? Would I be able to find happiness and fulfilment? And, was it realistic to expect that I would ever again be in good health?

I had been taking tablets for high cholesterol, high blood pressure and diabetes for over three and half years. I regularly took paracetamol and ibuprofen for aches and pains. I suffered with psoriasis and, to top it all, I was at least eight or nine kilos over weight. As far as I was aware - and what I had been led to believe by my doctor - I'd be taking the tablets for the rest of my life. My conditions would need to be constantly managed by prescription medicines and, worst of all, these would only get worse over time. I didn't believe for a moment that the vision Greg was talking about - the possibility of living a rich, rewarding, healthy life - could apply to me. However much I wanted to believe him, I couldn't see my life changing.

"Whatever you believe", said Greg, "will be true for you. For life to change, we must change, and the most important thing we need to change is our personal ethos. Why? Because your life reflects your beliefs. Whatever you believe about yourself and your life tends to manifest."

"A number of people have mentioned the ethos here," I said, "but I'm not entirely sure that I understand what it is."

"An ethos" said Greg, "is made up of core principles and personal values."

"You mean, like your conscience?" I said.

"Yes and no," said Greg, smiling. "Your ethos is actually much more than your conscience. Your conscience is set by your moral code, yes? What you believe to be right and wrong. However, your ethos extends to all of your social, economic, political...even spiritual values. For example, being friendly to people you meet wouldn't be the result of a moral code or a matter for one's conscience, but it would reflect your ethos. Everything we do and say, is ultimately a reflection of our ethos."

I nodded. "I think I understand." I said.

Greg smiled. "We wanted to promote a positive, empowering ethos to show people that, whatever their age or circumstances, life is always full of possibility. It's about empowering people to reconnect with their hobbies, pursue long lost dreams and desires. It's about doing what you always wanted to do but perhaps couldn't due to the pressures of life.

"The ethos is for anyone who feels like they're at a crossroads in their life. They might be retired, they might be semi-retired. They may be coming to the end of their career; their children may have grown up and left home. They may be facing a difficult and challenging time in their lives, and they may be questioning their future or their place in the world."

Everything Greg was saying resonated with me. The best times of my life were in the past. I couldn't begin to see how my life could ever be as good as it was years ago. How could it be otherwise? We all know that nothing, but wine and cheese improves with age. But, at the same time, Greg spoke with passion and conviction. What if there was a possibility that the years ahead could be as happy and fulfilled as years past? What if the best years of my life were still to come? What if happiness is not determined so much by our age, but by our ethos?

"Most people reach a point in their lives", Greg said, "when they experience a profound shift in their identity. For decades, their lives had revolved around work and family and, when work comes to an end and the children have grown up and start to make their own way in the world, there is a huge void."

"The ethos represents a different philosophy of life, one that enables people to fill that void." said, Greg.

"It's about recognising new opportunities, seeing new possibilities."

"New opportunities?" I said. What new opportunities could there be for people of my age?

"There are always new possibilities." said Greg. "But, we've got to look forward rather than back. We want to inspire people to live a fulfilling, active life through an ethos that gives them opportunities to continue to grow as people, to learn, to continue to enjoy new experiences and, most important of all, to make new friendships. We believe that, whatever a person's circumstances may be and whatever their stage in life, we can all pursue a dream. This is why we built Sun Park, and that is what the ethos here is all about."

Greg's words were certainly inspiring although, in truth, I still wasn't completely convinced. I don't know why. Perhaps it all sounded a bit too good to be true. And, as my late wife used to say, quoting Judge Judy, 'If it sounds too good to be true, it probably is.' But then, I couldn't help wondering; what difference would it make to my life - at this time in my life - if I did make new friends, tried new activities, and had new experiences? I could feel myself starting to feel excited. I had never heard of this kind of approach, this kind of ethos, especially for someone of my age. I didn't want to get my hopes up but, at the same time, there was no getting away from the fact that, in my current situation, I wanted - no, needed - to feel inspired.

I was in exactly the kind of limbo that Greg had alluded to; my children no longer needed me, I had no job and no prospects. I had some wonderful memories, but to dream of new possibilities was unthinkable at my stage in life. However, the longer I listened to Greg, the more I was beginning to think the unthinkable. Maybe, just maybe, there might be some hope for the future. But then again, I've heard a lot of bullshit in my life. Over the years I've learned the hard way that talk is cheap. I don't believe anything or anyone anymore without evidence.

"When we set out," said Greg, sensing my scepticism, "many people said we were crazy. Maybe we are. But it was the great Steve Jobs who said that 'those people who are crazy enough to change the world are the ones that actually do.'"

"You're changing the world?" I said.

"Of course. One person at a time." said Greg. "To many what we are doing may seem like foolish, idealistic nonsense. They don't believe what we're doing is possible. That's the reason we open the doors on Friday mornings. Anyone can come in and look around, meet the community, and see Sun Park for themselves."

"Why is it closed to the public the rest of the week?" I asked.

"It's a private, gated community, not a conventional hotel." said Greg. "We restrict access to one morning a week to respect the privacy of our members and guests. For some, it has become their second home. But, whether someone is here for a week, a month or a year, it wouldn't be fair to them to allow a constant flow of people wandering through the grounds. One of the things we value is the safety and security of our members and guests."

It was certainly intriguing. I looked around at all the people gathered on the terrace. They all seemed normal, friendly people. But, first impressions could be misleading. And, there was one question that kept niggling away in my head: would I fit in?

Then, as if reading my mind, Greg said, "Stan, sometimes life is like a watermelon. It's looks hard, it feels hard but, someone, somewhere, took a risk and broke into it, and discovered that it's a deliciously sweet fruit."

What did I have to lose? What was the worst-case scenario if I decided to come back here for a week or two? A few weeks of sunshine, living a few minutes' walk from the beach. Not much of a loss! And then I thought, what might be the best-case scenario? I could end up meeting new people, perhaps make some new friends.

I cannot remember the last time I tried a new activity. If half of what Greg was saying was true, it could turn out to be quite an adventure. Certainly, by coming back, even for a short stay, I would be able to find out exactly what the ethos was all about. In the end, the ethos was the deciding factor. If it was as everyone had claimed, if life at Sun Park was as Greg and the others I had met that morning had described, it could be life-changing.

I didn't need to give it much thought. After all, in my situation and, at my time of life, what did I have to lose? I had one question: how do I book?

Chapter 4: Every day Is An Awakening

*'If every day is an awakening, you will never grow
old. You will just keep growing.'*
Gail Sheehy

The plane landed at 10:30pm in the evening at
Arrecife airport. Within fifteen minutes, I was
through customs with my luggage and walking out of
Arrivals to the awaiting mini-bus. The bus driver
checked my ticket and smiled. *"Vamos en vente
minutos, señor."* My face must have given away the
fact that I didn't speak Spanish. Inside the bus a
female voice translated, 'It departs in twenty
minutes'.

The journey from the airport to Playa Blanca took just
half an hour the first time I came but, on this
occasion, the bus made two detours to drop off five
other passengers and it wasn't until an hour later that
I finally arrived at Sun Park.

Although it was past midnight, the street was well lit.
I recognised the area immediately. I took out the
printed email I had been sent which contained
instructions on accessing the resort. A security code
was needed to open the side entrance gate. Once
through, I was to make my way to the reception area
and find a small, key box behind the counter.
Another code was required to open it. Inside the safe
was an envelope with my name on it which contained
the keys to my apartment. It seemed straightforward enough and, if I had any difficulties, there

was a voice-activated help port, a brilliant talking device that had been designed using the latest artificial intelligence technologies. I tested it out. "Hi" I said.

The machine replied, "Welcome to Sun Park. What's your name?"

"Stan Davis."

"Welcome Stan. How can I help you?".

"Can you tell me how to get to my apartment?" I said.

"Stan, your apartment is number 209. Walk out of the main doors to the terrace, turn left, walk down the stairs and then continue straight ahead. Head towards the second block on your left. Apartment 209 is on the ground floor, second from the end. Would you like me to send a map to your phone?"

"That would be great, thanks."

"Please note that you'll need to access the WiFi. The network is 'Sun Park' and the username and password is 'welcome', all lower case."

"Thanks." I said, forgetting that I was talking to a machine.

"You're welcome, Stan." came the reply. Some machine!

I accessed the wifi on my phone. Instantly the phone pinged and a message with a link appeared. The link opened a navigation map. Incredible!

"If you have any problems, Stan, just pop back." said the machine. "I'm here all day and night. And, if I can't help you, I will be able to pass you through to a live operator."

"Thank you." I said and picked up my bags.

"You're welcome, Stan. Have a good night."

I shook my head. Technology can be amazing.

I walked through the double doors onto the main terrace, as instructed.

"Hey Stan! Welcome back!". I recognised his face immediately. It was George, one of the crowd I had met from my visit on Social Friday. He was sitting on one of the wicker sofas holding a Kindle.

"Hi George. Thanks. Good to see you."

"How was your flight?" he said, standing up to shake my hand.

"Fine, thanks."

"We were expecting you over an hour ago." he said.

I explained that the airport bus had taken a few detours along the way to drop some people off at another resort.

"Well, you're here safe and sound, and that's all that matters." he said.

"What apartment have you been allocated?" he said.

"209" I said. "I think it's down to the left. I've just got a map on my phone."

"Ah. Alexa. Of course." he said. "You won't need that. I'll show you. It's not very far."

"Thanks." I said.

"Here, let me help you with your bags." George said. I had noticed trolleys outside reception, but I only had a carry-on bag and a suitcase which had wheels on it so I didn't bother with a trolley. George took my suitcase and led the way. "Follow me," he said.

George led me out to the terrace, down some stairs, through the gardens and past a swimming pool to a Chiringuito bar. A few men and women were still up having drinks.

'Hi guys.' said George. 'This is Stan. He's just arrived. Stan meet Steve, Alan, Betty and Jackie.'

"Welcome, Stan. How long are you here for?" asked Steve.

"Just a couple of weeks" I said. "What about you guys?"

"We're all here for a few months" said Steve.

"A few months? You must like it here."

"It's a home from home!"

"If you fancy a nightcap, we're here for a while."

"To be honest, it's been a long journey and I'm ready for bed. Can we catch up tomorrow?"

"Of course. Have a good night."

George ushered me on, up some steps, along the path to the penultimate apartment on the ground floor. "This is it." he said. The front door led straight through to the lounge and kitchenette. On the table was a bowl of fresh fruit. "These are grown here on the resort." George said.

A small corridor led from the lounge to the bathroom and bedroom. George flicked the light on in the bathroom, which was tiled in small aqua blue and white tiles. He then turned on the light in the bedroom. "The evenings can get a bit chilly this time of year," he said, "but there are extra blankets in the cupboard if you need them." He opened the built-in wardrobes. "Here they are." He turned to me. "That's it. I'll let you settle yourself in. Have a good night, Stan."

"Thanks so much, George." I said, "I really appreciate your help."

George smiled. "It's my pleasure."

I slept comfortably and was woken early by the sound of birds outside my bedroom window. The island is famed for the colonies of exotic birds that migrate from the Northern hemisphere in the winter months. The Hoopoe birds, identified by their black and white wings and brown bodies, inhabit the island along with grey doves and numerous species of smaller birds. Together, they make quite a dawn chorus.

Looking out of the window, the day had already begun. Back home in the UK, it would still be pitch black at this time of day, but on Lanzarote the sun had begun its ascent. I got out of bed feeling a little stiff. The bed was comfortable. The problem was my back; it had been bothering me on and off for years and, in recent months, it had been getting noticeably worse. I cursed myself for leaving the Ibuprofen back at home and made a mental note to buy some later in the day.

I walked into the lounge, made myself a cup of tea, and went outside. Being west-facing, my terrace was in the shade. However, I noticed some tables and chairs in the middle of the gardens that were already in sunshine, a perfect place to drink my morning tea. I sat alone, closed my eyes and faced toward the rising sun. Bliss!

CHAPTER 5: LIVING WITH INTENTION

'You don't climb mountains without a team, you don't climb mountains without being fit, you don't climb mountains without being prepared and you don't climb mountains without balancing the risks and rewards. And you never climb a mountain by accident - it has to be intentional.'

Mark Udall

"Good morning!". I looked up to see an athletic, bald man, his head tanned and shaved, walking toward me. He was wearing a black tee shirt and black oriental cotton trousers, the kind you see worn by people who practise martial arts.

'Good morning', I replied.

"Hi, my name's Josh." he said, offering his hand.

"Hi Josh. I'm Stan."

"Pleased to meet you Stan. When did you arrive?"

"Just last night."

"Great. How long are you here for?"

"Just a few weeks." I said. "How about you?"

"This is my third week" he said smiling. "I'm here for a total of three months though."

A man approached from the building in front of us. He was a good foot taller than Josh but he had a much smaller frame.

'Good morning, Gordon." Josh said. "This is Stan. He arrived last night."

Gordon offered his left hand and it was only then that I noticed that the lower part of his right arm was missing. A small section of his upper arm which extended from his shoulder ended in a rounded stump in what looked like a tiny incomplete hand. It looked to me like Gordon had been a victim of the Thalidomide scandal back in the late 1950's and early 60's.

I knew about it because my mother had been prescribed the same drug when she was pregnant with me. Fortunately for me, a family friend advised my mother not to take it. Had that friend not intervened, I could have been afflicted with the same condition.

Gordon noticed me glance at his deformity. "That's my bowling arm" he said with a smile.

Josh put his hand on my shoulder. "Hey, Stan, fancy joining us? We've got a Tai Chi class starting in a few minutes."

I hesitated. "I don't know anything about Tai Chi."

'This is your chance to find out then," said Josh smiling.

"I didn't know anything about Tai Chi before I came here either," said Gordon. "It's one of the best things I've done though. Trust me!"

I can't say that I'd ever been interested in Tai Chi or anything similar but, with Gordon's glowing testimony, I found myself agreeing to give it a go. "Okay. Why not?", I said.

'Fantastic!" said Josh. "We do it just over there." he said pointing ahead. I turned to look and could see a dozen or so people already beginning to congregate.

~

Despite my reservations, I thoroughly enjoyed the class. I felt slightly awkward at first, but as soon as I realised that, of the thirty or so people who participated, over half were beginners like me, I felt a lot more at ease. The session began with a 'guided visualisation' where we visualised each part of the body relaxing. This was followed by stretching exercises, and then we rotated all of the joints from the neck down to the ankles. At that point, Josh took us through the Eight Step Tai Chi 'form', a series of slow, flowing movements, much like a dance. To an onlooker, it looks like an oriental version of line dancing. Although the movements are slow and relaxed, they are also purposeful and require concentration. By the end of the class - which lasted forty-five minutes - I really did feel as if something had changed. It was probably all in my head, but the stiffness and ache in my lower back had gone.

I walked over to Josh. "What did you think?", he said.

"I thoroughly enjoyed it." I said with complete sincerity. "I'm not sure if it's my imagination but my back pain has eased up."

"That's not uncommon." Josh said. "Tai chi is one of the best ways to release mental and physical tension, and this almost always leads to noticeable improvements in both muscle and joint pain. It's amazing what changes occur once we start to breathe deeply, release tension in the muscles and allow energy to flow around the body as it should. The joints start to move more freely and this explains why so many people report that their aches and pains seem to disappear."

Josh explained that Tai Chi doesn't just alleviate physical tension. It is a form of meditation through movement. Harvard Medical School refer to Tai Chi as 'medication through movement'. It helps people focus their minds.

"Scientists estimate that we have between 60,000 and 80,000 thoughts every day." Josh said. "That's around 2,500 every hour, and most of those thoughts are *exactly* the same as the ones we had yesterday! Tai Chi, like meditation, gives your mind a chance to be still. *Tranquillo* as the islanders say. It's sort of like a reset."

Josh picked up his things. "What are you up to now?", he asked. "Would you like to join me for a coffee?".

~

Josh's apartment was less than twenty metres from where he taught the Tai Chi class.

"Please, take a seat." he said, as we reached his terrace. "What can I get you to drink?"

"Coffee would be great", I said.

"I only have soy milk" he said. "Is that okay?"

"I take my coffee black, thanks."

A few minutes later, Josh brought out a jug of fresh, filtered coffee, and a plate of fruit and biscuits. I asked him how he had discovered Sun Park.

"I came to a Social Friday, like you", Josh said. "I was staying nearby and saw an advert in a magazine, and I thought it sounded interesting. Simple as that, really."

"And you obviously like it here?" I said.

Josh smiled. "Like it? I love it! I love the place, I love the people and, of course, I love the ethos."

"I heard a lot about the ethos," I said. "But, what specifically is it about the ethos that you love?"

"One key aspect for me is the focus on intentional activities."

"What are 'intentional activities'?" I asked.

Josh explained that psychologists have discovered that there are three things that are responsible for how happy we feel - our genes, our circumstances, and intentional activities. "Here's how it works," he said. "Each of us is born with a predisposition to a certain level of happiness. It's called the genetic set point. Basically, it's a level of happiness programmed in our genes. Think of it like a baseline where your happiness tends to stabilize, regardless of what happens to you in life."

I'd never heard this before. "Happiness is set by our genes?" I said.

"Partly, yes. According to researchers, our genes account for somewhere between thirty-three and fifty percent of our overall happiness at any one time. But, of course, there are other factors."

"What, like where we live and our finances? I said.

"Yes. Although, believe it or not, money and material possessions have very little effect on our overall happiness."

"Seriously?" I said.

"Yes. In all of the studies ever done on happiness, money has never been shown to account for more than two percent."

"Hmm. You honestly believe that?" I said, still unconvinced.

"It's not a question of belief" said Josh. "It's been demonstrated in hundreds of studies all over the world. Once we're earning enough to cover our basic needs and comforts, anything more has very little influence on our happiness. Yes, we may feel excited when we buy a new car or house or when we get the latest smartphone. But, that doesn't last.

Within a short time, we find ourselves right back at the genetic baseline."

"I've never been particularly wealthy in my life, so I wouldn't know." I said. "But, I would have thought that if you could afford the lifestyle of the rich and famous, you'd have a better chance of being happy."

"It's an illusion." said Josh. "In fact, the circumstances of our lives account for less than ten percent of our happiness. And that includes our job, our health, our income, our religious beliefs, our age, gender, and our home environment."

"Really?" I said. I was genuinely shocked and made a mental note to verify this for myself later.

"So, we're looking at up to fifty percent of our happiness in life being determined by our genes and another ten percent being affected by our life circumstances." said Josh. "But - here's the good news... forty percent of our happiness is attributed to the 'intentional activities'. What are they? Well, they include those activities that involve physical exercise like tai chi, yoga, walking, dancing, swimming, tennis, cycling... you know, any physical exercise. This is because physical exercise causes the body to release chemicals called endorphins. These endorphins interact with the receptors in your brain which alleviate pain as well as trigger a positive feeling in the body, like that of morphine. The old adage is true; the healthier you are in body, the happier you are in mind."

I nodded. I'd heard that before although it had never motivated me to become more active. I don't know why.

"Of course, there's a lot more to intentional activities than physical exercise." Josh continued. "Intentional activities include more mental and emotional activities like meditation, music, singing, art, even playing cards. Things for which we develop a passion."

"I suppose that makes sense." I said.

"There are other intentional activities that are not quite so obvious." said Josh. "The two dominant ones are random acts of kindness and expressing gratitude. Both have a huge effect on how happy we feel."

My expression must have given my cynicism away. "Seriously," said Josh. "Believe it or not, gratitude has been shown to increase our happiness by twenty-five percent or more! You can find out more about it in the expressive writing workshop."

"Expressive writing?"

"It's just one of many workshops that are run from time to time. You're in luck because I saw there is a new course starting this week. Trust me on this, it can be life-changing."

"When you put it like that, how can I not go?" I said.

"The workshops and seminars are held in the Learning Annex." Josh said. "I think the next course starts the day after tomorrow. It involves just twenty minutes each day. You'll find details on the community noticeboard."

~

After leaving Josh I headed to the main reception to look at the noticeboard to see what intentional activities were available. Each day of the week was crammed with events and activities ranging from the movie evenings, group outings and organised day trips, to bridge club, dance classes, sports, games, hiking and cycling. A typical day would start as early as 8 o'clock with swimming, tai chi, yoga or Pilates, followed by a virtual constant flow of activities and community events. From early morning until late in the evening, there is always something to do and people to do it with.

~

At first glance, the noticeboard looks no different to one that you'd expect to find in many holiday resorts. It is, after all, just a list of the daily and weekly activities. However, there is one thing that differentiates the noticeboard at Sun Park from any similar notice boards that may be found in the neighbouring hotels; many of the activities and events are run by and for guests, members and visitors alike.

"The activities are central to the ethos here," Greg had told me. Activities bring people together, he had said. "When we play together, learn together and even work together, we are happier and healthier than when we do these things by ourselves."

I hadn't participated in any kind of sport since I had been at University. My adult life was centred around work. By the time I got home at the end of the week day, I didn't have the time or energy to do much else other than watch TV and maybe surf the internet. I know I could have joined any number of clubs at the weekend, but there were always things to do around the house, or the garden, or shopping. I know this might come across as an excuse. Of course, I could have done much more. Here, at Sun Park, looking at the noticeboard, I had no excuse not to try some of the activities. The options seemed to be limitless and I was determined to get involved and try at least some of the activities. After all, I had nothing to lose, many of them were free of charge.

As I stood reviewing my options for the day, I became aware of a woman standing beside me. She was full figured woman dressed in khaki shorts and a blue baggy tee shirt. Her name was Jeannie and she was staying at Sun Park for the winter.

"Are there always so many things going on?" I asked.

"Pretty much." she said. "And the great thing is, if there is something you want to do that isn't on the board, all you have to do is post it. You know? Invite people to join in your activity and chances are, people will turn up."

"Really?" I said. "It's that simple?".

"Sure." Jeannie smiled. "During my first week here, I was alone and one evening I thought about going out into town for a Chinese meal. The only problem was that I didn't fancy sitting in a restaurant by myself. So, I posted a notice on the board asking if anyone fancied coming out for a Chinese."

"What happened?"

"Twenty-two people turned up!" she said.

"That's astonishing."

"That's Sun Park! Now we post all kinds of events and outings. Most weeks we all go out for a picnic at the beach. Everybody brings wine and drinks and nibbles, and it is a great laugh. Often, we all end up swimming in the sea at midnight."

"Sounds like fun." I said. "I can't ever remember swimming in the sea at midnight. What's it like?"

"You'll have to come next time to find out." she said. "Oh...by the way, we're going on an outing next Tuesday. If you don't have any plans, why don't you come along?"

"Erm, I'm not sure." I said. Truth be told, I hadn't planned on going on an outing. I wasn't closed to the idea, but group outings had never really appealed to me. "Where are you going?", I asked.

"Jameos del Agua" she said. "Have you ever been?"

"No."

"Then you must come!" she said. "It really is something to see. The coach is nearly full, but we've got a few spaces left. It'll be fun."

"When you put it like that" I said, "How can I say 'no'?"

~

Later, I discovered that Jeannie's story and mine were not dissimilar. She had discovered Sun Park three years earlier because, like me, she had been made redundant. And, like me, she had come on holiday to Playa Blanca to clear her head before deciding what she was going to do next with her life. However, unlike me, Jeannie had come on holiday with a friend. The two had stayed at the neighbouring French-owned hotel and, after the first two weeks of a month-long trip, they stumbled upon Sun Park.

"We'd ventured out to the beach on some days and, in the evenings, we walked into town and ate in some of the beachfront restaurants. But, it had been just the two of us. I don't think we spoke to anyone else in our time there

"Then, as luck would have it," said Jeannie, "I was reading one of the local magazines and came across an article about Sun Park."

I smiled to myself hearing how Jeannie's story mirrored my own experience. "I was intrigued," she continued. "I mean...holiday-living, and being part of a community? I'd never heard anything quite like it before. I showed my friend, and we agreed to visit the next Friday to take a look around and see for ourselves."

"And, what did you think?" I said.

"Well, put it this way," said Jeannie, "by the time we got back to our hotel, which was literally next door, both my friend and I had said that we'd like to come back and stay at Sun Park for a week. Just to try it out. We came back and, before that week was up, we extended our stay."

"Really? How long for?"

"Three months!"

"Seriously?"

"I'm not joking," she said. "And, the three months turned into six, and here we are now - three years later - and I'm still here."

Aside from a few trips back to the UK to see her family, Jeannie and her friend had never left Sun Park. It was now her home. "I rent my house out in the UK." she said. "And the rental income more than covers the cost of living here at Sun Park. I mean here there are no extra bills, no rates, no utilities. There's nothing to pay apart from the standard weekly or monthly charge."

I thought about it briefly, and it started to make sense. Was that something I could do? I'd need to do some research as I had no idea what rental income my small terraced house could generate.

"Of course, there are other options too." Jeannie said. "We've got super-fast internet and some people run their entire businesses from here. They attend teleconferences online, run webinars, arrange online meetings. All they need is a smartphone or laptop."

I had been at Sun Park for less than a day, so it was far too early for me to start thinking long-term but, after reviewing the noticeboard and talking to Josh and Jeannie, already I was beginning to feel that I might want to stay at Sun Park for more than the two weeks I had booked.

CHAPTER 6: A PLACE LIKE HOME

*'Where we love is home - home that our feet may
leave, but not our hearts.'*
Oliver Wendell Holmes, Sr.

I fell into the Spanish custom of having a Siesta on my first afternoon at Sun Park. This quickly became a habit that I grew to love. I'd never been one for napping during the day but, at Sun Park, I became a fan. A half hour lying on a sunbed, in the shade, by the pool or on my terrace would re-energise and re-invigorate me for the rest of the day and well into the evening. I don't know if it was the siesta or the lifestyle, but I found myself able to do so much more during the day than ever before.

It was after that first siesta that I met Veronica and Don, a couple from Cambridgeshire in the UK, who had made Sun Park their primary residence. They still owned their house back in the UK, but they had chosen to spend most of the year at Sun Park. I met them whilst I was walking around the resort, trying to get my bearings, late in the afternoon. Veronica was sitting on the terrace outside their apartment. She smiled and said 'hello'. I quickly learned that being friendly and welcoming is a central element of the ethos at Sun Park. Unlike most other places where people are reticent to open up to strangers, at Sun Park, a stranger is often referred to as a friend that you haven't met yet. This is why, when people at Sun Park meet a stranger for the first time, they will always engage in conversation. Meeting new people and making new friends is a large part of what makes Sun Park so special.

To my surprise, Veronica invited me to stop for a drink. "I've got tea, coffee, water or, how about a glass of wine?".

It was 5:30 in the afternoon. Too early for a glass of wine? "It's never too early for a glass of wine." Veronica said, smiling. "What would you prefer, red or white?"

"Red would be fantastic." I said.

"Red it is. Have a seat. I'll be with you in a minute." Veronica said, gesturing to the empty chairs on her terrace.

A man appeared from inside the apartment pushing himself in a wheelchair. He had an amiable disposition, someone to whom anyone would take an immediate liking. "Hello" he said. "I'm Don."

I introduced myself. "When did you arrive?" he said.

"Late last night."

"And, how are you settling in?" Don asked.

"So far, so good." I said.

Veronica reappeared holding three glasses and a bottle of Rioja. "Here we go." she said and began to pour out three glasses.

Veronica and Don had first come to Sun Park three years ago following a friend's recommendation. Don had been diagnosed with Multiple Sclerosis only a few years earlier and his symptoms were worsening in the UK. They had been considering spending more time in a warmer climate and a friend suggested that they take a look at Sun Park. They researched the area and the resort and decided it was worth investigating. "The price was reasonable," said Veronica, "the weather is as close to perfect as you'll find anywhere in Europe, and then, of course, there was the ethos."

Veronica and Don were devout Christians and knew the value of being part of a community. "We looked at the Sun Park brochure and website and it was as if it had been made for us." Veronica said.

"I thought it looked too good to be true." said Don, "but it was everything we hoped it would be."

"And more." said Veronica. "Everyone is so friendly. The climate is perfect. It's safe. It's easy for Don to get around, isn't it love?".

"Yep." Don said. "Thanks to all the ramps, I can get everywhere with these wheels."

I had noticed that there was a rampway next to every set of stairs. These days you'd expect wheelchair access in most resorts, but Sun Park had been designed to ensure that everywhere had wheelchair access.

"It's very easy for us living here." said Veronica. "Initially, I thought it would be somewhere we could come and just enjoy ourselves. But, it became our second home. We feel safe here and Don is so much better for being here.

"The apartments here are just the perfect size. Don can get to the bedroom and the bathroom and kitchenette by himself with minimum effort. More importantly, we are surrounded by friends."

"That's true" said Don. "I don't know whether it is the weather or the friendly atmosphere or the sense of freedom that I have here, but there's no question that I'm much better when I'm here. I've halved my medication too!"

Veronica explained that Don had an infection the previous week. "Whenever he gets an infection, he can hardly move. He can't move his legs. He can't even raise a cup to his lips. When it happens back in the UK, I have to call an ambulance or get neighbours to help me, if they're at home. It can be very difficult. When it happened here, I had ten people on my doorstep all ready and willing to help within a matter of minutes."

I took a sip of wine. "That's incredible." I said.

"The doctor's office is literally next door." Veronica continued. "We had the antibiotics Don needed within ten minutes. Literally, the whole thing took less than twenty minutes, and we were back in our apartment. In the UK, we'd still be on our way to hospital."

"I think this is one of the best choices we've made in our lives." Said Don. "I used to be in the Royal Air Force and got stationed all over the world. But, here is special. You get the weather, lots of activities, friends, and you're part of this amazing community. What more could you ask for?"

Just then, a tall blonde woman wearing shorts and a vest passed by the terrace. "Hi Jenny." said Veronica. "How are you?"

"Fine thanks Vee."

"Jenny, this is Stan. Stan, Jenny."

Jenny stepped onto the terrace to shake my hand.

"Can I get you a drink?" Veronica asked.

"Thanks. Just a water, please."

Jenny sat down at the table next to me.

"Jenny is our neighbour." said Don. She was a beautiful woman by any standard. She had long blonde hair, a smooth tanned complexion and large blue eyes. She had first come to Sun Park about the same time as Veronica and Don, a little over three years ago. She had lost her husband, Geoffrey, to whom she had been happily married for forty-six years. Prostate cancer had taken Geoffrey after a long and difficult battle. In the end, he had died peacefully, but Jenny struggled to cope without him. Losing your life partner after five decades would be a massive loss for anyone to bear, and Jenny had no desire to try and rebuild her life. She was seventy-one years old and, as she and her husband had never been able to have children (a result of her suffering from ovarian cancer), aside from distant relatives who lived in Toronto, Jenny was very much alone in the world.

Jenny's loneliness became magnified as the Christmas holidays approached. "I was feeling more and more depressed at the thought of spending Christmas alone for the first time in nearly fifty years." she said. "I knew I needed help, so I made an appointment to see my GP. I thought my doctor would be able to prescribe some pills or recommend a therapist. As fate or luck would have it, whilst I was in the GP's waiting room I read an article about Sun Park. 'Independent togetherness...an enriching, supportive community...warmth and friendship". I read it, and read it and read it again. And, then I thought, 'Well why not go for it?'. So, I came out by myself for Christmas."

"That was brave." I said. "I mean, being a single woman travelling alone."

"I thought so too." she said, with a beaming smile. "I'd never gone anywhere by myself before and, to be honest, at first, I was a bit like this". She motioned with her right palm facing downward, rocking in a gesture of uncertainty.

"I assume, as you're still here, that you had a good time?", I asked.

"Good is not the right word." she said. "It was wonderful. Really wonderful! It was like being in one big, loving, happy family. I met so many lovely people. Everyone was just so friendly. There were quite a few who were on their own, but it didn't matter because we were all together. I found a new best friend too; Gillian, who is also a widow. It was just so nice being able to talk to someone else who had been through what I had.

"On Christmas day, everyone took food down to the Marigold bar and we all shared a huge Christmas lunch together. I say 'lunch' but we didn't sit down to eat until around 4pm. Then, in the evening, we all walked down to the beach with wine and nibbles and sat and watched a firework display. It was just fantastic."

Jenny had booked to stay at Sun Park for two weeks over Christmas and New Year but, after the first week, she had extended her stay for an additional four months. Now, she spends most of her time there. "Before coming here," she said, "I thought my life was over. Then I came here and discovered that, far from being over, a new life was just beginning."

Sun Park was 'home' for Veronica and Don and Jenny, and many others. My mind went back to an article in the in-flight magazine that I read on the flight over. It was about people's perceptions of travelling abroad and their feelings about coming home at the end of their trip. In it the writer had reflected on the place that we all think of as 'home'. It was over two thousand years ago that the Roman philosopher, Gaius Plinius Secundus, (also known as Pliny the Elder or just Pliny to his friends) coined the phrase 'Home is where the heart is.' But, what does that mean? Is your home where you live? Or where you were born? Is your home where you were raised? Or is the place you think of as your home somewhere else?

The answer was revealed by research carried out at the Pew Research Center back in 2008. The researchers interviewed 2,260 American adults and asked people where their home was located. The question read: 'what is the place, in your heart, you consider to be home.' The answers were startling; only twenty-two percent said that their 'home' was where they currently lived. Just twenty-six percent reported that 'home' was where they were born or raised, and a mere eighteen percent regarded 'home' as the place that they had lived the longest. Fifteen percent said that their 'home' was the town where their family had come from, and four percent said that home was where they had gone to high school.

The researchers discovered that, for the vast majority of people, 'home' is less about a physical connection to a specific place, and more about the *feelings* we associate with a place. Home is not necessarily where we live today or where we lived yesterday, or even the place where we grew up. Home is not defined by time, but rather by feelings. It is the place to which we attach our strongest emotions, where we feel safe and secure, and in control. Pliny had been spot on, home is where the heart is.

Perhaps this explains why Veronica and Don, and Jenny and everyone who spend most of the year at Sun Park, had come to regard it as their 'home from home'. It ticked all the boxes; this is where they feel a deep sense of belonging. I wondered whether, in time, I'd come to think of Sun Park in the same way.

CHAPTER 7: BEING FREE

'Be more concerned with your character than with your reputation. Your character is what you really are while your reputation is merely what others think you are.'
John Wooden

I left Veronica and Don just as the sun was beginning to set. I looked at my watch and was astonished to discover that I'd been sitting with them for over one and a half hours. The time had flown by as it tends to do when you're absorbed in conversation and enjoying yourself. I was conscious not to outstay my welcome, so I thanked them for their hospitality and made my way back to my apartment.

As I passed the main terrace, I came across a man sitting alone on the main terrace. He had a tanned, rugged complexion with unkempt silver-grey hair, light blue eyes, and short, silver stubble rather than a fully-grown beard. Back at home, men half his age pay good money and probably spend more time in the bathroom than their wives and girlfriends, all to achieve the same look. He had a slim, athletic build and was wearing washed out, denim shorts, a cotton light grey tee shirt and flip flops. My first impression was of a seasoned sailor or cool, surfer dude. It turned out that, in this instance, I was right. Joel Hurst, is an avid surfer from Cornwall in the UK.

Joel raised his hand and said, 'Good evening'.

I offered my hand and introduced myself.

Joel and his wife had been coming to Sun Park every year since it opened. "I did some communal living when I was younger," he said, "but when you're younger there's a lot of ego involved. Here everyone is older and wiser. We've reached the stage where we've had a lot of corners knocked off us by life and that kind of makes it easier. Ego doesn't really matter to us anymore.

"My wife and I had been talking about living abroad for a long time. 'Wouldn't it be great if a bunch of us bought a place.' we said. People do it. But, it can get complicated."

"How do you mean, complicated?" I said.

"I guess with finances and legal stuff. But, here it's easy. You can dip in and out when you want. There are some people who come and treat it like a rest. You know, they don't do anything but sit out in the sun and they don't get involved in anything. That's fine. There's no obligation to do anything. But, the funny thing is, even the most private, introverted people seem to come out of themselves after a week or two. They find it's more enjoyable to sit and drink a glass of wine with friends than sit drinking by yourself."

"That's true." I said. "So, you come here because you like being part of a community?".

"I come here because I love being with friends but there's more to it than that. Here I feel completely free." he said. "I just love the vibe. You know? Everyone is so friendly. The climate is just perfect and the sea is great for me 'cause the waves can get up a bit and I love to surf.

"But aside from those things, what I really love about this place is that it is based upon libertarian principles."

"What do you mean by that?" I asked.

"In a nutshell, Libertarianism is about freedom. Which means, so long as you don't harm others and are respectful and considerate, it's nobody's business what you do."

"Sounds reasonable." I said.

"And that's what we've got here." Joel said.

"But there are rules, aren't there? I mean there are list of things specified in the welcome booklet, right?"

"Sure." said Joel. "But all of the rules here are either required by the laws of the land or they're necessary to protect the rights and enjoyment of other people staying here. Which is a good thing. For example, you can't smoke indoors. That's partly because it is against the law to allow people to smoke indoors but also, if you were to smoke indoors, it would very likely interfere with the enjoyment and rights of the next person to occupy your apartment because there is no escaping the foul odour and stains that smoking cigarettes causes to furniture and fabrics."

I nodded. This libertarian philosophy appealed to me too. I liked the idea that you're free to come and go as you please, of living freely, without obligation. Perhaps that's why so many people love being at Sun Park; it offers everyone the opportunity to be free in a way that isn't always possible in the real world.

CHAPTER 8: THE LAW OF THE FEW

'We cannot seek achievement for ourselves and forget about progress and prosperity for our community... Our ambitions must be broad enough to include the aspirations and needs of others, for their sakes and for our own.'
Cesar Chavez

In his bestselling book, 'The Tipping Point', Malcolm Gladwell discusses 'The Law of The Few' which is a theory that any kind of social change is heavily dependent on the involvement of a few people with 'a particular and rare set of social gifts'. Jacob is one such person. He is what Gladwell refers to as a 'connector'.

Connectors make it their business to connect with everybody and they never miss an opportunity to make introductions within their social circle or community. They are outgoing, exceptionally warm and friendly people, who link all of us up with the rest of the world. Within any social movement you find these Connectors, usually numbering just a handful of people who have an extraordinary knack for making friends and acquaintances. These are people, Gladwell says, who have a special gift for bringing the world together.

Jacob had been the first person I met when I arrived at Sun Park on Social Friday, and he had instantly made me feel welcome, offering me a drink, taking the time to get to know me, and then introducing me to some of his friends. The next time I bumped into him was on my second morning back at Sun Park. I was walking to the Cafe when we crossed paths. I was touched that he remembered me.

"Stan! How lovely to see you!" he effused.

"You too, Jacob." I replied.

"I heard you were back", he said. "How have you been?"

"I'm doing well, thanks." I said. "I arrived two nights ago and I'm just feeling my way around."

He asked me where I was going and, when I said I was on my way to the cafe, without any hesitation he said "Please. Come have a drink at my place."

"Are you sure?" I asked, slightly taken aback at his hospitality.

"Of course. It's just over there." he said pointing to the corner of the quadrant. "Come, I've got tea, coffee, what you like?".

Jacob's apartment was situated at the far end of the resort. Like mine, it was on the ground floor, the only difference being that his terrace was south-facing and his garden had been lovingly tended, boasting an assortment of colourful plants. To the side of the building he had a line of pots in which he was growing tomatoes and peas. On the terrace, Jacob had a small two-seater sofa, and a coffee table with two easy chairs. There was an easel with a jar full of paint brushes positioned in the corner.

It was easy to see that Jacob's apartment was also his home. The walls were covered with richly coloured oil paintings, and he had filled the apartment with his own furniture, and installed his own cooker and floor-to-ceiling fridge-freezer. Within a few minutes, a full Mediterranean breakfast was laid out on the table. Freshly squeezed orange juice, sliced and diced cucumbers and tomatoes, hummus, olive oil, pita bread, avocado and a selection of cheeses. A far cry from the milk and cereal I was used to back home. "Coffee or tea?" he said.

"Coffee would be great, thanks."

Jacob told me his story. He and his wife had divorced after thirty years of marriage. It hadn't been easy for either of them. "Sometimes you grow so far apart and want such different things that to separate is the only solution" he said.

After he and his wife separated, Jacob looked for a fresh start. "A new beginning!" as he put it. And that had led him to Sun Park. "I have three sons and a daughter." He said. "They live in different countries and on different continents. I visit them when I can, and we all stay in touch on Skype, which is wonderful. But, I have my own life too. Here I can do the things I love with my friends."

"What do you do?"

"I love to paint, and I love working with clay. So, I spend a lot of time in the art studio."

"Ah, so these are your paintings?" I said pointing to the walls.

"Yes. What do you think?"

There was an assortment of images ranging from African tribal women to still art and local landscapes, but they shared the same technique and style, generous brush strokes and bright colours. The leaning towards abstract rather than simply recreating an exact replica of the subject is, I think, more interesting than an exact pictorial representation because it represents different things to each viewer.

"That's why I love slightly abstract" he said. "You and I see the same thing but we have different perceptions. It's like Life, yes? We judge something from our experience. We see through our eyes but we interpret through our brain." Jacob pointed to a landscape painting of the coast. "If someone has never seen the sea before, what would this represent to them?"

It was an interesting point. I had no idea of the answer.

"We can only see things through our frame of reference. Here, look at this," he said, handing me a postcard drawing of a young woman. "What do you see?" he asked.

"What do you mean?" I said. "It's a young woman, right?"

"Yes…and no." he said. "It depends the way you look at it." He outlined part of the image and said, "This is a nose, here is the mouth…" Suddenly, I saw an old woman. "My goodness!"

"Exactly!" Jacob said, beaming. "This is a well-known perceptual illusion credited to British cartoonist W. E. Hill, who published it in 1915 as 'My Wife and Mother-in-law?' with the caption 'They are both in this picture — Find them!' And, now you've found them!"

"This is work of an artist," he said. "To encourage people to stop and reflect on life." said Jacob. "To have an open mind and look at things from a different perspective."

Jacob had rediscovered his love of painting at Sun Park and went on to do sculpting and pottery. "I used to love to paint years ago, but then family and work took over and I had no time," he said. "Now, I am no longer Jacob the engineer. I'm Jacob the artist!".

Jacob had an infectious enthusiasm, not just for his art, but for life. He loves his life, he loves meeting and connecting with people, and he loves to give. "Giving is living" he said. He was regularly buying exotic plants, which he didn't limit to his little garden patch. Like many others, he enjoyed tending to and enriching all of the gardens around the resort.

We walked over the art studio where he showed me the kiln he had donated and there on the tables were pots and jugs and small sculptures that members had created in his classes.

"Groups come over from the UK during the summer months for art holidays," he said, "because everything they need is here. We've got the studio and, as you can see, it is heaven for landscape artists.

"Have you ever painted?" he asked.

"Not since school. Funnily enough, I got an A grade in my art exam, but I've forgotten everything."

"I doubt that," said Jacob, "art never leaves you. You must try it whilst you're here. You might fall in love with it again, like I did."

~

The following afternoon I went along to the art class. Twenty people turned up and Jacob was among them. We split up into two groups, one group stayed in the studio to paint still life and the other, which I joined, went out to draw landscapes. Our group walked past the marina and beyond the Volcán Hotel, and set up on the cliff top. "How magical is this?" said Jacob. The coast to the east contained enclaves with white-washed buildings nestled between the cliff tops. Seagulls flew overhead, there was a cool, westerly breeze. It was as close to perfect as I could imagine.

I sat on a bench with my sketch pad, and sat momentarily paralysed in front of the blank page, unsure where to start. I hadn't done anything like this since I was child. The leader of our group, a woman called Linda, seeing my hesitation came over. "You okay, Stan?"

"To be honest, I'm not sure where to start."

"Some people start by creating a grid, maybe four or eight sections." She said. "This helps maintain the perspective of what you're drawing. Then just start and see where the image takes you."

An old memory from my youth came into my head. I'm sitting in the school hall at the start of a history exam ruminating about how to start an essay. Five minutes pass, other students are writing furiously, and I feel panic rising inside me. How do I start my essay? If I continue to prevaricate, the paper will remain blank and I will fail. I take a deep breath, pick up my pen and write as if I am talking to a friend and the words come. It is as if the essay is writing itself.

I picked up my pencil and started to sketch, lightly at first, but with each stroke the lines and shades become bolder and more confident. Gradually, the page began morphing into an image. I became completely absorbed in the drawing. Like the essay, the image seemed to be forming itself. It wasn't going to win the Turner Prize, but it was something I had created. One of the first things I had created for many years.

I felt a tap on my shoulder. Astonishingly, two hours had passed. Where had the time gone? I'd forgotten how engrossing drawing could be.

~

Aristotle wrote that the point of art was not to represent the outward appearance of things, but to convey their inward significance. Looking at some of the other people's drawings, I think understood what Aristotle meant. We had all drawn from different perspectives, each highlighting different things in the scene. Several people had included a yacht anchored off the shore, something which I had completely missed. At the same time, my drawing included a row of villas in the distance that some of the others had not recorded.

The significance of a piece of art depends as much on the perspective and focus of the observer as the object itself, Linda said. We discussed this as we walked back to Sun Park. Why do we look out at the same scene yet see different things? "Two men look out through prison bars; one sees mud, the other sees stars," laughed Jacob. "We see through the eyes, but we interpret through the brain." I guess that is what makes a shared experience so much richer than a solo experience; other people enable us to see and experience things that we might not have noticed had we been there alone.

Later that evening I opened my sketch pad and reviewed my drawing and I compared it to a photo I had taken with my camera. My style was more Lowry than Turner. The proportions were a little off and there were numerous things I had missed completely. However, what made the drawing interesting – at least to me - were the things I had noticed and how I had recorded them. Although I have created many more drawings and paintings since that day, that first one remains special to me because it captured an afternoon when I rediscovered an appreciation for art. It was a memory never to be forgotten.

CHAPTER 9: THE MARIGOLD

'Together we can face any challenges as deep as the ocean and as high as the sky.'
Sonia Gandhi

The Marigold Bar is one of the hubs where people tend to congregate at Sun Park, especially if there is some sort of entertainment like a supper-quiz, a concert or a show. If an event is going on at night and you aren't sure where it is being held, ninety-nine times out of a hundred, it will be in the Marigold.

The Marigold isn't just a place where people congregate in the evenings. It is frequently used during the day too when it doubles as a members' lounge. It's also used as a venue for some activities, particularly on the odd occasion when the weather is either too windy or hot to do an activity outside. The Marigold is an obvious alternate venue because it is such a huge room. I would guess it encompasses somewhere in the region of two hundred and fifty square metres. It includes a four metre purpose-built drinks bar, enough chairs and tables to accommodate well over two hundred people, a raised stage, and off to the far side is an area that houses a large flat screen TV which people use to watch sporting events and movies.

The Marigold was named, rather aptly, after the movie, *The Best Exotic Marigold Hotel*, which, by coincidence, was released the same year that Sun Park re-opened its doors. There were some obvious parallels in the storyline of the movie and Sun Park.

In the movie, a group of disparate British retirees (Judi Dench, Maggie Smith, Bill Nighy) decide to outsource their retirement to India. Lured by advertisements for the newly restored Marigold Hotel and imagining a life of leisure in exotic, lush surroundings, the group arrive to find that their new home is not quite as they had imagined. The hotel is in a state of disrepair, a far cry from their creature comforts at home in the UK. Slowly, the group fall in love with the hotel and its slightly eccentric but big-hearted manager, a young Indian man with big dreams. Rallying together and overcoming the challenges facing the hotel and its manager, one by one the guests find happiness, love and a renewed zest for life.

When Sun Park launched its new self-service concept in 2012, the first guests had arrived at a place that was, like the Exotic Marigold Hotel, rather shabby in appearance. But, what it lacked in terms of appearance, was more than made up for by the community ethos. As in the movie, guests at Sun Park had bought into Greg and Christina's vision, and they had all rallied together to make that vision a reality.

One of their first tasks was to turn the run-down former hall into a bar and lounge. Over several days, they had cleared, cleaned and decorated the entire space. It can't have been an easy feat, especially when you bear in mind the size of the room. Carson and his wife, Clare, were there at the time. "You wouldn't believe it," Carson said. "There were dead cockroaches and a large hole in the floor. All the furniture was covered in dust, there was no electricity and no water in the washrooms.

Everything needed to be scrubbed, the plumbing renewed, and the walls and ceiling desperately needed a coat of paint."

The Marigold was transformed by paying guests, many of whom had come to Sun Park for a holiday. Some had gone for a few weeks, others had turned up for months. One can imagine what some people would have thought turning up at a resort that needed so much renovation. The paths to the south side were covered with weeds to the point where you couldn't pass, the gardens were a wilderness, straight out of a spaghetti Western; the swimming pools were empty, save for a few feet of water covered in algae. And that was just for starters.

However, those people who had the courage to stay after walking through the gates and seeing how badly the place needed a makeover, said that they had received much more than they had given. Like the visitors to the Exotic Marigold Hotel, those first guests at Sun Park had enjoyed a life-changing - no, life-affirming - experience. They had found friendship, a community that exuded generosity of spirit, and renewed *joie de vivre* that many were not even aware had been missing from their lives.

It must have been quite a sight; all these people coming together, working together, to transform an expanse that, by all accounts, had been unused and neglected, into the modern and homely members' lounge that it is today.

I have to confess that when I walked into the Marigold Bar for the first time - by myself, still new to the resort and not knowing many people - I felt a little self-conscious. It was a Tuesday evening and there were quite a few groups of people sitting at different tables.

I walked over to the bar to get a drink. I discovered that every evening the bar was manned by volunteers. That evening the bar was being tended by a couple, Maureen and her husband Alan.

I introduced myself. "I thought the bar was self-service?" I said.

"It is most of the time." said Alan, "but some of us take turns in the evenings to help out. Otherwise, there'd be a bit of chaos with so many people trying to get their drinks at the same time."

"That's very good of you." I said.

"Not really." said Maureen. "We're happy to do it. It means we get to chat with a lot of people through the evening."

I was impressed that a group of members took it upon themselves to manage everything in the Marigold. Without those volunteers, the community would have to pay for cleaners to come in and clean the bar every day. That would mean higher prices but, perhaps more importantly, it would also remove the opportunity for those who wanted to contribute.

"So, Stan, what would you like to drink?" Maureen said.

"Is there a Guinness?" I asked.

Maureen turned to look at the prices on the board. "It appears there is." I put the coins into the honesty box and Maureen handed me a pint glass, and a can from the fridge.

"Thanks so much" I said.

I turned around and a man sitting among the crowd of people on the table ahead looked up.

"Hi, there" he said. "How are you?"

"Fine, thanks." I replied. "You?"

"I'm good too, thanks." he said.

I moved towards him and only then noticed that he was sitting in a wheelchair. He offered me his left hand, his right hand was controlling the chair.

"I'm Dennis." he said.

"Hi Dennis." I said, pulling up a chair.

Dennis is a remarkable man. Born in the 1950s, he was crippled at an early age by poliomyelitis, a virulent disease that swept through much of the Western world at that time. The Polio virus is carried exclusively through human faeces which is why the best prevention is actually through improved hygiene and clean water. Healthy people who become infected tend to be asymptomatic, yet a small percentage of people remain vulnerable and, according to the official data from The World Health Organisation, one in a hundred can be severely afflicted. For the weak, and especially infants with underdeveloped immune systems, Polio can have devastating effects, spreading like wildfire through the body, causing muscles to atrophy, sometimes within hours or days. As fate would have it, Dennis was part of that one percent.

The Polio virus took hold of Dennis' body shortly after he turned four years of age. All he remembered was that one morning he fell over and couldn't stand up. Then, his memory jumps to what may have been weeks or months spent locked away in a hospital isolation ward.

"I don't remember much other than being alone, day after day, in a sterile room, separated from my family." he said. It's difficult to imagine how traumatic that must have been. I knew a little about separation simply because my parents separated just after my sixth birthday. But, whilst I couldn't be with my father who had moved abroad, I still had my mother and my siblings. I wasn't alone and isolated from my entire family like Dennis had been. All I could say was "I'm sorry. That must have been tough."

"It was," said Dennis. "But I never realised how tough it was or how deeply it affected me until I came here."

"Here?" I said. "Why is that?"

"Last year I signed up for an Expressive Writing workshop and it all sort of came out there."

I was intrigued. "Josh mentioned that course to me too." I said. "What was it like?"

"Amazing" he said. "It involves writing for twenty minutes on four consecutive days. Each day you're told to write about something that still brings up strong emotions."

"What kind of things? I asked.

"Literally, it could be anything that is troubling you; a person, an event or experience you've had in the past. It could also be something that's still ongoing in your life, and it could also be something that might happen in the future."

"Ah" I said. "I see."

"The only rule is you have to have strong feelings relating to anything you're writing about. Anyway, when I signed up for the workshop, I had no idea what it was all about or what I was going to write about, but it all just happened. These feelings I had locked away just resurfaced."

"And that was a good thing?" I asked, unsure what possible benefit could result from re-living the things that caused anguish.

"Absolutely." said Dennis enthusiastically. "I'd never really allowed myself to think about that part of my childhood before, and it was the first time I'd really expressed my feelings about that time in my life. The chap who ran the workshop explained the science behind it. It's real therapy. I won't bore you with it now, but if you get the opportunity whilst you're here, check it out."

"I will." I said.

As a teenager and young adult, Dennis had managed to walk with the aid of crutches, but now, in his sixties he relied on his motorised wheelchair to get about. He explained that he had come to Sun Park because he had heard that it was wheelchair-friendly and that the activities were open to all, regardless of ability.

"What sort of activities do you like doing?" I asked.

"My favourite thing is tall ship sailing." he said.

"Tall ship sailing?" I repeated. "You mean the big, old sailing ships?"

Dennis laughed. "Yes."

"Seriously?"

"Yes."

In any other setting, I would have thought he was joking. "How..." I was trying to think of the right words to ask how a wheelchair-bound person could sail on a tall ship. I've seen tall ships up close in Greenwich and on videos. Oftentimes, they're moving fast through the sea tilted at an angle anywhere between ten and thirty degrees because, being a sail boat, they're propelled by the wind.

"Have you ever heard of the Jubilee Sailing Trust?" Dennis asked.

I shook my head.

"Well, google it sometime. It's incredible. People of all ages and abilities - and disabilities, of course - sail together. Everyone is treated the same, no matter who they are or what condition they're in. It is fantastic!"

"That sounds phenomenal." I said. And I truly meant it. I took out my notebook and made a note to check it out later.

"How long have you been sailing tall ships?" I asked.

"Oh, over twenty-five years." he said. "I was having some physical therapy and I overheard someone talking about a sailing trip he'd been on, and the thing was... he was far worse off than me in terms of physical ability. I mean, he could only use one arm. I thought to myself, if he could do it, surely, I could too. So, later that day, I looked it up and sure enough, it was all true."

"But how do you...you know... get around on one of these ships. I mean, they're beasts, right? It's not like being on a cruise liner."

Dennis picked up his beer, and took a sip. "You're right there," he said. "It's proper sailing all right, but the ships are fully equipped and fitted out. Being in a wheelchair isn't a problem."

"It sounds incredible." I said. "I can't even begin to imagine how you do it? Moving about on deck on a wheelchair can't be easy. How do you go below deck? Or the rigging? Don't tell me you get up on the rigging?"

"Yes, we all get up the rigging too." he said, still smiling. "They've thought of everything."

"I have got to check it out." I said.

"You should." said Dennis. "It is one of the best things I've ever done. It gives you a great sense of satisfaction. You know? Like you've accomplished something. There is something wonderful about overcoming challenges."

I drank some of my Guinness momentarily reflecting on the fact that here I was able-bodied and yet never had I even entertained the idea of doing anything as challenging as that. It had been like that for most of my life. I'd always taken the safe, easy path. In my youth there were times when I chose not to do an outdoor activity because I was so self-conscious. In later life, I reasoned that my physical health wasn't good enough or, other times, I used family responsibilities as an excuse to stop me from trying something new.

Perhaps we all need challenges to feel alive? I mused. What challenges or obstacles had I overcome in recent years? I had got by, yes. I'd survived the loss of my wife. But, what else? Nothing came to mind. I had been stuck in the same loop, like some Groundhog Day; get up, go to work, come home, eat dinner, watch a bit of TV, go to bed, and start all over again. Up until this moment, I'd let myself believe that it was too late for new challenges but, speaking with Dennis, listening to what he had achieved and the challenges he had overcome, I realised that there really wasn't anything stopping me from being more adventurous in my life.

If someone like Dennis, with his disability, could spend a week on board a tall sailing ship and somehow manage to do the same jobs on board that able-bodied people did - including going up and down the rigging - then there shouldn't be anything holding me back from pursuing new challenges in my own life.

Dennis was largely confined to a wheelchair, yet he had an enthusiasm for life that I envied. He took another sip of beer and continued. "The thing that I love most about sailing with the Jubilee Trust" he said, "is the same thing I love about Sun Park."

"What's that?" I asked.

"The inclusiveness." he replied. "Everyone is treated the same. It doesn't matter if you're able-bodied or not, it doesn't matter where you're from or what religion you were born into, or how much money you have. None of that matters."

I thought about what Dennis was saying. Back in the UK people tend to be judged by their appearance - their skin colour, tattoos and piercings, the brand of clothes they're wearing, the car they drive, the house they live in. If the appearance doesn't fit, and a person don't meet our criteria, they're excluded. Then there's the matter of their background, their accent, their profession or trade. But, here at Sun Park, there were no such judgements, everybody was welcomed, everyone was included. Greg would always say, "all that matters is what you feel in your heart".

After a momentary pause, I asked Dennis what activities he did at Sun Park.

"Let's see. Where to start?" he said. "There's Pétanque, mini-golf, table tennis, meditation. I play Bridge, go on walks..."

"Walks?" I said.

"Well, wheelies, I suppose." he said smiling. "The able-bodied walk and I wheel. The promenade along the front stretches for miles and miles and is mostly flat so it's perfect for me. I get exercise, fresh sea air, and great company. We all chat amongst ourselves as we go... and we end up stopping for coffee and cake somewhere."

"Sounds great." I said.

"It is!" replied Dennis. "We're going tomorrow morning if you fancy it. There's a local market up by the marina. We usually stop there for a mooch and then continue on beyond the lighthouse to a little cafe on the edge of the sea."

"I'm in." I said. "What time?"

"We all meet in the reception at 10am and head off. We're usually back around lunchtime."

"I'll look forward to it." I said, and I meant it.

CHAPTER 10: MARKET DAY

'I cannot even imagine where I would be today were it not for that handful of friends who have given me a heart full of joy. Let's face it, friends make life a lot more fun.'
Charles R. Swindoll

The following morning, as soon as the Tai Chi class had finished, I went back to my apartment, had a shower, put on fresh clothes and made my way to the reception. I managed to get there just as a crowd of people were beginning to move towards the exit. I recognised a few faces, and then saw Dennis.

"You made it, then!" he said.

"Of course. You made it sound unmissable" I said. "And I'm only here for a couple of weeks." A woman beckoned Dennis over from the other side of the room. "Excuse me, Stan. I'm being summoned." he said. "That's my fiancée".

"She looks like a keeper." I said winking. "I'll catch you later."

I heard someone behind me call my name and recognised the Irish accent immediately. It was my pal, George, with his wife, Evelyn. George welcomed me like an old friend, with a hug. "You remember my wife, Evelyn?".

"Of course. How are you, Evelyn?". The last time I'd seen Evelyn was several weeks back when I arrived on Social Friday. She had been among the group I ended up chatting with for most of the morning.

We did the Spanish greeting, kissing on both cheeks. George then introduced me to his friends; Jim a seventy-three-year-old accountant from Worthing, Sussex, was accompanied by his daughters, Kirsty a tall, attractive blonde woman from Kent and Krystal, who had mousy-brown hair and was slightly shorter. Next to Jim, was Pippa, who I also remembered from Social Friday. Pippa had been my tour guide that morning.

It was another beautiful day outside. Another clear, blue sky. However, there was a slight chill to the wind which was more noticeable when walking in shade. Still, I didn't need any more than the shorts, tee shirt and sandals I was wearing. It was an unfamiliar feeling, walking down the road towards the promenade, part of a group that consisted of over twenty people. The curious thing was that, although I didn't know any of the group well, I felt as if I was among good friends. Less than ten minutes ago most of these people had been strangers to me, and yet I felt very comfortable among them.

I thought of my first trip to Lanzarote, weeks earlier, when I had stayed at a nearby hotel. I had walked along the promenade numerous times during that week, but always on my own. It was the same beach, the same sea air and the same sun, but walking as part of a group was vastly more enjoyable than walking the path on my own.

When we reached the beachfront, it was already alive with tourists. There were a few people swimming in the sea. I wasn't sure why anyone would want to step into in the sea in the winter months. The sun is warm, but I had dipped my toes into the water the day before and it had been bitterly cold. However, call it courage or insanity, a few days later I did end up swimming in the sea and, when I was in, I understood completely what made people run into freezing, cold water. It made you feel alive.

~

I'm not sure I would have attempted to dive into the sea at that time of year had I been on my own. It was so cold a man could lose his manhood for the rest of the week. However, I met a Scotsman called Ross outside the gates of Sun Park. Ross was a huge man who could have been a heavyweight boxer in his youth, and he talked me into joining him to take a dip in the sea. He was on his way out, and holding the gate open for people going in. Even though I didn't know him from Adam, he said hello and we started chatting. I noticed he was carrying a towel and asked him where he was going. "For a swim", he said in a broad, highland accent.

"Isn't a bit cold?".

"Aye, t'is that." Ross said laughing. "Takes a mad Scotsman to go in the water. Or, a mad Englishman!"

Five minutes later I had put on swimming trunks, grabbed a towel and was walking down to the sea with my new mad Scots friend.

One of the things I've learned during my time at Sun Park is never to judge a person by their appearance.

Looks can be deceiving. With his shaved head and large frame dotted with some random tattoos on his arms and legs, Ross had an imposing, if not intimidating, presence. If you came across him at night on the streets of Dundee, you could be forgiven for wanting to cross to the other side of the road. But, as I said, looks can be deceiving, and in Ross' case, they most certainly were. He was one of the most gentle, friendly, warm personalities you could wish to meet. This was also reflected in his career. He was a carer and worked nights looking after people who suffered with mental health problems. Five days a week, he would leave home at nine o'clock in the evening, drive the best part of an hour to his place of work and put in a ten-hour shift before returning home the following day.

"That can't be easy, not just looking after people, but working through the night." I said.

"T'isn't easy," said Ross, "but everything is just a state of mind, no? And, somebody has to do it."

Ross didn't do his job out of necessity. Yes, like the rest of us, he needed a job, but he could have chosen from dozens of alternative options. He did the job, he said, because it was important. The people he cared for needed help and support and, despite the antisocial hours, he loved his work. For as long as he was able, he said, he would continue doing it. Week in, week out.

When Ross and I reached the sea, he ran in shouting "Heid doon, arse up!". A mad Scots' phrase which loosely translates to 'Get on with it!'. Not wanting to appear the wussy Englishman, I followed him into the water. For a moment, I had to catch my breath. I couldn't remember ever having been so cold, but at the same time, I hadn't felt so alive in a long time.

Ross and I made a dip in the sea a daily ritual. A mad Scotsman and an even madder Englishman. Very possibly there were holidaymakers walking along the promenade looking down and wondering what two middle-aged men were doing wading in the icy Atlantic waters in February. All I can say is, don't knock it until you try it. But, make sure you try it with a friend.

~

Walking along the promenade heading towards the local market with Dennis and the rest of the group, the sea glistening in the sun, I felt something that I hadn't felt for a very long time. Happy. More than happy, carefree.

Kirsty and Krystal, Jim's daughters, were bubbly characters. They were both married but had come over together to be with their father to celebrate his seventy-second birthday. Jim was a regular visitor to Sun park. He returned every year and stayed for 3-6 months at a time. This was his third visit. "He's a bit of player." Kirsty whispered. "He's got a girlfriend back at home and some of the ladies are itching to get their claws in."

"He goes dancing with one, plays Bridge with another..." laughed Krystal.

"Good for him." I said. "And which one does he...erm."

"We're still trying to work that out." said Kirsty, giggling. "Dad keeps his cards very close to his chest."

~

It took less than fifteen minutes to walk to the market, which was held in the streets backing on to the marina. I was amazed to see what must have been over a hundred stalls selling anything and everything from fruits and vegetables, local cheeses, cakes, nuts and honey to knick-knacks, dresses, swimwear, toys, kitchenware, bespoke jewellery, and hand-made ornaments. Kirsty headed straight to the fake designer handbags.

"Come on, Kirsty." said Krystal. "You bought three last year."

"You can never have enough handbags, can you, Stan?" Kirsty said winking at me.

"But, two of them fell to bits within a few months!" said Krystal.

"And, that's why I need some more." said Kirsty as she rummaged through the Gucci and Armani lookalikes.

"Is that what they call female logic?" I said.

"No, that's what you call the mad bag lady!" said Krystal.

Kirsty had put aside three handbags. The total cost was €110. "I give you €50" she said to the vendor.

"Ninety-five" was the first comeback, but after much bartering, they agreed on €65.

"That's impressive haggling." I said.

"Thanks. I've had a lot of practise," said Kirsty, who was very pleased with her purchases.

"How are you even going to get those bags home?" demanded Krystal. "You haven't got a suitcase to put them in." Kirsty then turned to me. "We only came with hand luggage," she said shaking her head. "I'll tell you what, Dad." said Kirsty. "I'll come back next month with a suitcase and I'll take them home with me."

Jim smiled. "Fine with me." he said.

"That's assuming they haven't fallen apart by then!" said Krystal. "Dad, what is she like!"

~

As we walked around the market the group slowly dispersed, some browsing, some buying. However, an hour or so later we met up at the Cafe Puerto for coffee and a sandwich. It was there that Kirsty and Krystal mentioned the dance class being held that evening in the Marigold. "Not for me, I'm afraid." I said. "I've got two left feet."

"That's okay" said Kirsty. "I've got two right ones!".

"You've got to come to make up the numbers" Krystal said and, being lost for a plausible excuse, I agreed.

CHAPTER 11: YOU CAN DANCE

'When you dance, your purpose is not to get to a certain place on the floor. It's to enjoy each step along the way.'
Wayne Dyer

Most evenings at Sun Park, you'll find people dancing, usually they'll be in the Marigold Bar, but occasionally they'll be outside at the Ching-Ching Chiringuito. For those like me who don't dance, help is at hand. One night each week, dance classes are available for all, regardless of age or ability. I discovered these classes were often raucous, joyous affairs, filled with laughter, as everyone attempted to learn a series of moves which were demonstrated by community members, Howard and Celia. The classes cover various types of dance, from classic ballroom to the Latin American salsa and so forth. On the night I went along, they were teaching 'Ceroc', a hybrid style that incorporated Jive, Lindy Hop and Rock 'n Roll.

Howard was quick to point out that he wasn't a trained dance instructor. "I'm not a professional or anything." he said. "But I have been dancing all my life so, when I'm here at Sun Park, I'm happy to show people a few moves."

I'm no dancer. I've got about as much rhythm as a constipated baboon. So, it was with immense trepidation that I went along to the class. I had been cajoled, in the nicest possible way, by Kirsty and Krystal who were accompanying their father, Jim, who was by all accounts an accomplished ballroom dancer. The girls insisted that I was needed to 'make up the numbers' but, when I arrived, there were plenty of other men taking the class, so my presence wasn't as necessary as the girls had led me to believe.

I walked into the Marigold bar bang on eight o'clock to find more than sixty people waiting for the class to begin. Before I could even consider making an inconspicuous U-turn, the two instructors, Howard and Celia, took to the stage and asked all the men in the room had to form five lines. The women then stood in lines opposite the men, and the few extra women formed into partners.

Howard and Celia may not have been professional teachers, but you'd never know. They certainly knew how to dance. They stood on the stage and demonstrated a few moves, one by one. Ceroc isn't difficult, but it isn't easy either. Howard held Celia and walked us through each move; one - two - three - step - one - two - three - step. The room was full of laughter as we all tried to memorise each sequence of moves. After a few dry runs, Howard turned on his iPod and we danced the moves in time to music. A minute or so later, Howard said 'Change partners! Ladies move down six places.' All of the women moved down the line and stopped at the sixth man from where they stood, and we started all over again, going over the moves and adding new ones.

The process was repeated; each sequence of steps was demonstrated, practised and then performed to music. Each time, I found myself facing a new partner. I discovered that dance classes are not just a fun form of exercise, they are also a fantastic way of meeting and getting to know a lot of people in a short space of time. The formal instruction ended after half an hour or so, and then everyone was free to practise the moves to Howard's playlist or just dance freestyle.

I must say that, much to my surprise, I thoroughly enjoyed the evening. By the time the music finally stopped, I felt as if I'd done a circuit at the gym. I'd never have dreamed of going to a dance class by myself back in the UK, but it really was a lot of fun. I still couldn't dance, but I'd learnt a few moves and I felt more than a little proud of myself. I would never have imagined in a million years that I'd want to learn to dance, and I'm sure that if you asked anyone who knows me back home whether they thought they could picture me participating in any kind of dance classes, they'd laugh. I guess that once you lose your inhibitions, you find yourself open to trying new activities, and you never know where a new activity will lead.

The dance class came in handy on Friday night when I joined a whole crowd of 'Sun Rockers' - the name by which many of the regulars at Sun Park were often referred - and headed down to Barney's, everyone's favourite local drinking hole. Barney's is situated a quarter of a mile down the road in a small beachfront complex. It is a cafe-come-burger bar in the day, but on Friday nights, it transforms into an intimate gig venue, the music being performed by Barney himself, owner and raconteur, together with some of the locals.

The range of musical genres is astonishing. Barney and his friends move effortlessly from Rock 'n Roll, to Swing, Classic Pop and Country. When they get to my all-time favourites, they are mesmerising. The Beatles, Genesis, Supertramp, the Doobie Brothers... I could sit and listen to Barney and his cohorts play all night. They really are that good. Sometimes, Eddie, who runs the Sun Park cafe, will get up and sing a few numbers. You'd never know to talk to him, but Eddie can hold his own on stage with the best of them. Boy, can those guys play. Never off key, and they transport you back in time, belting out the old familiar tunes.

Every Friday night, a little after 10 pm, when most people their age back in the UK are making a hot drink and getting ready for bed, you'll find a troop of guests from Sun Park making their way down to party at Barney's. And, when I say party, I mean party with a capital P. They're not ones for just sitting around. They're pushing back chairs and up on their feet putting the dance moves they've learned from Howard and Celia to the test. If you are ever in Playa Blanca on a Friday night, head down to Barneys and chances are you'll see a crowd from Sun Park dancing and singing along into the early hours.

I walked down with Jeannie, her friend Melanie, and a chap I hadn't met before called Michael, a tall, thin man from Glasgow. Michael had an angular face with a long, narrow nose, thin lips. He wore thick-rimmed, black glasses which made his eyes look small and, out of habit or discomfort, he kept resetting his glasses on the bridge of his nose. He was quietly spoken and had a slight lisp.

I wasn't sure whether Michael was staying at Sun Park because I hadn't seen him at the resort. However, as we walked along the road, he explained that he had only arrived earlier in the day, and he was staying for just five days.

"Why five days?" I asked.

"I just thought I'd try it out." he said.

"Fair enough." I replied. "I'm only here for a couple of weeks myself. What's your impression so far?" I asked.

"It's okay, I suppose." Michael said. "I don't know if it's for me though."

When we arrived at Barneys, I went to the bar to buy a round of drinks for Melanie, Jeannie, Michael and myself. The women moved straight onto the dance floor, but I decided to stay at the bar to talk more with Michael. There seemed a sadness about him. His shoulders were hunched and, when he spoke, for the most part he looked down, preferring to avoid eye contact. As we chatted and with a second bottle of Coronita, he began to speak more freely and began looking at me, rather than at the floor.

Michael explained that he had come to Sun Park alone because, like me, he had few close friends back home. He was an unexceptional man who had lived an unexceptional life. He had worked his entire adult life at the Post Office, sorting post and, on occasion, delivering it. He hadn't had an unhappy life but, from the way he spoke, it hadn't been particularly happy either. He was single, and had never married. I asked him why, and he just shrugged.

Michael was an only child. Both of his parents, devout and very strict Christians, had passed away and he had no extended family. "Actually..." he paused, his mouth poised to speak, but no words came. He took a breath and continued, "Actually, I'm adopted."

I took a sip from my beer, and let him continue at his own pace. "I only found out seven years ago... by accident." he said.

I was intrigued. How does someone find out something like that by accident?

"I was sitting in the kitchen with my mother and a neighbour," he said, "and the neighbour was talking about one of her friends whose son, she said 'was adopted like Michael'. I was confused. I didn't know what she was talking about. But then my mother gave the woman a 'look'. You know? Telling her to 'shush'. It was only then that the penny dropped."

"How did you feel about it?" I asked.

"I don't know." he said. "I couldn't believe it. It was a complete shock."

"Did you find out who your birth parents were?", I asked.

"Yes and no." he said. "I never found out who my biological father was, but I did track down my birth mother. It took me a little over a year to trace her though."

"What happened?"

"Nothing. She had passed away three years earlier." His eyes seemed to well up.

"I'm so sorry", I said putting my hand on his shoulder. There was not much I could say. We stood there in silence together listening to Barney's rendition of Supertramp's masterpiece 'Even in the Quietest Moments'...

> *But still the tears keep falling*
> *They're raining from the sky*
> *Well there's a lot of me got to go under*
> *before I get high*

A few moments later, more Sun Rockers started to arrive. I introduced Michael to some of the others. Then the mood changed as Barney began playing Van Morrison's 'Bright Side of The Street' and our Eddie picked up the microphone and took on the role of lead singer. He could certainly sing too.

I felt a tap on my shoulder. It was Celia, "Fancy a dance, Stan?". A week ago, I would have said 'Sorry, I can't dance', but that wasn't an option now. I may have been as awkward as a new-born fawn, and I only knew the seven steps we had learned in the dance class, which I had to mix and loop, but... I could dance. And I would dance the night away with anyone who asked.

CHAPTER 12: WHAT PRICE HONESTY?

'Honesty is the most single most important factor having a direct bearing on the final success of an individual, corporation, or product.'
Ed McMahon

Friday afternoon. Jacob and Jeannie had invited me and a few others out for coffee and cake in the marina. The first restaurant offered generous slices of apple or cherry pie along with a large mug of coffee or tea. I opted for the cherry pie and lemon tea. When the pies and drinks arrived, I reached into my pocket to pay. A mild panic came over me as I went through all of my pockets. The wallet was missing.

"What's wrong?" Jacob said.

"I don't have my wallet."

"No problem." he said. "I've got mine. You're my guest today," and he patted me on the shoulder.

"Do you remember where you left it?" said Jeannie, aware that I was more than a little anxious. The wallet contained over a hundred euros in cash and, more worryingly, all my credit and debit cards.

I thought back to earlier in the day, trying to think of when I last had it. I had paid for a drink at the cafe in the morning, but there was no other time I could remember needing it.

"Shit!" I said. It dawned on me that I'd left it on a table, outside the cafe on the main terrace.

"It's not a problem." said Jacob.

"It's got all my cards and cash." I said, and I stood up.

"Seriously, Stan." said Jacob. "Trust me. Enjoy the cake and coffee. It'll be fine."

I sat back down, not wanting to appear too alarmed, but I couldn't mask my concern. I ate a slice of cherry pie and tried not to think about my wallet. Jacob was right about one thing; there wasn't much I could do at this point. My wallet had been left on the table for nearly five hours. Chances are, it would be gone by now. I resigned myself to reporting the loss to the local Police station and hoping that my holiday insurance would cover at least some of the loss.

~

A little over an hour later we were back at Sun Park. I went ahead of the others and made my way to the table where I left the wallet earlier in the day. Just as I suspected, my wallet had gone. I went inside to the cafe. Eddie was cleaning the counters. "Hi, Stan. Everything okay?"

"Actually, no. I lost my wallet. I'm pretty sure I left it on that table this morning." I said, pointing to the table on the terrace.

"Is this it?" said Eddie reaching below the main counter. He put my wallet on the counter. "I found it when I was clearing up. I was about to put up a notice on the noticeboard."

"That's it!", I said. "Thank you so much!".

"You're welcome." Eddie said smiling. "Don't worry, it'll all be there." And it was. The cash, the cards. Nothing had been touched.

Jacob walked into the reception with Jeannie. "Well?", he said.

"You were right." I said. "Eddie had it."

"You see!" said Jacob. "You could leave the crown jewels, and nobody here would take them."

A few years ago, I read an article in the Guardian newspaper in the UK that revealed that less than one in a hundred wallets or purses lost in cafes, bars and restaurants ever get returned to the rightful owner. Once you lose your wallet, they say, you can kiss it goodbye because you're more than twice as likely to win betting on a single number on a roulette table. Yet, here at Sun Park, I had experienced first-hand that those statistics don't apply. If anything, the situation was the complete reverse. That may be because honesty is a key element of the ethos.

I remember being impressed the first time I walked into the Marigold Bar. It's a beautiful, spacious bar, not quite a Starbucks or Nostros, but cosy in its own way with enough comfortable chairs and tables to sit well over a hundred people. The bar itself was fully-stocked with alcoholic and non-alcoholic drinks, as well as a wide assortment of teas and coffees. It was certainly worthy of any cafe you'd find in the City of London. I could see why it was well used by the community. But, what impressed me more was the notice on the bar counter:

'Dear friend, please help yourself to whatever you want. You'll see the prices listed on the noticeboard. Just pay whatever the price is for the items you consume before you leave. Thank you for being honest, and have a great day!'

The bar is open 24/7 and, most of the time, there is nobody there to take your money or check that you pay the right amount. Imagine walking into a fully stocked pub or bar or cafe in your home city and finding that there's nobody behind the counter. I'd never seen anything like it, and couldn't help wondering if it would work in the real world.

When I googled it later, I discovered that one shop owner in Yorkshire had tried the 'honesty box' model. It was Boxing Day, the day after Christmas, and the shop owner, a man by the name of Tom Algie, wanted to spend the festive period with his family and he also wanted to give his three members of staff the day off. However, being the only convenience shop in the village, Tom didn't want to let his customers down. So, after giving it some thought, Tom came up with a solution that most business owners wouldn't dream of entertaining; he left his shop open and unattended for the entire day and relied on the honesty of his customers.

Inside, on the counter, he left a notice wishing season's greetings to all of his customers and informing them that they could help themselves to whatever products they wanted, but they should leave a note of the products purchased along with the money in the 'Honesty Box' which he left beside the note.

December 27th, the day after Boxing Day, Tom returned to the shop and found £173 in the box along with notes of all the products bought. What he hadn't banked upon was the notes of heartfelt thanks and season's greetings that customers left him. Astonishingly, Tom's plan had worked.

It is unknown whether the festive time of year had any influence on the customers' honesty, but would the honesty experiment work in a big city? I had my doubts. One thing I do know is that honesty is highly prized at Sun Park, and it works. Almost everything on sale is purchased this way. Need to wash your laundry? Shove the dirty clothes into a machine and put a few euros in the honesty box. Need to print a document? Use the complimentary computers in the tech room, print your document, and leave the requisite payment in the printing box. Want a drink from the Marigold or the Ching-Ching Chiringuito? Take a glass, and put your money in the box.

"Why are people more honest here than out there in the real world?" I asked Greg one day.

"Dishonesty comes in two forms - stealing and lying. Neither of which make a person feel good about themselves unless, of course, that person is a sociopath." he said.

"We believe that honesty is essential for success and happiness in life. We believe that most people want to be honest. We're all happier when we're honest. So, why are people at Sun Park honest? I think it comes down to the ethos."

~

It's a sunny, bright October morning. Unusually mild in London for the time of year. I've just come out of Old Street station and turned left past the coffee shop on the corner of Leonard Street. In my haste, I bump into a woman and my coat gets splattered with her coffee. She apologises profusely and, mortified at having doused me with her latte, she fusses over me, cleaning the excess milky liquid off my coat. She finishes wiping my coat down, and apologises for the fourth time. I tell her it's fine. I'm in a hurry to get to work. Before I've walked ten metres, a feeling of sickness comes over me. Why was the coffee cold? I put my hand on my left jacket pocket. My phone is gone. I feel for my wallet in my back pocket and that is missing too. I'd been mugged.

Ever since that day, I've been wary of strangers. It got much worse with stories of knives and violent attacks. If a stranger stops me in the street, whether to ask me for the time or for directions or to participate in a survey, I rush ahead ignoring him - or her. If someone says 'hello' and I don't recognise their face, I move ahead pretending not to have heard.

I have learned to distrust people. I don't think that one mugging made me this way. One of the first things we're all taught as children is 'Don't talk to strangers'. It isn't safe. As I grew older, I learned that distrust wasn't something to be reserved for strangers. A few years back, a close friend discovered that his wife had been having an affair with her boss. It had gone on for three years. Three years! How do you move forward in a relationship with that? How can you trust a person again?

~

One of the best definitions of trust I've come across, certainly one of the most beautiful, is the one given by Charles Feltman in his book, *The Thin Book Of Trust*. 'Trust', he wrote, 'is simply choosing to make something that is important to you vulnerable to the actions of someone else.'

When we trust, we make ourselves vulnerable. We can be hurt, which may be why we don't tend to give it away freely. Trust, for most of us, must be earned.

I read long ago that trust can be likened to a bag of marbles. You collect a marble from someone every time they do or say something that demonstrates loyalty and friendship. The more marbles you collect from someone, the more you trust them. Trust is earned over time, but it can also be lost in a heartbeat. One act of betrayal, and the bag is sliced through, all the marbles fall to the floor and, try as you may, they can't be put back in.

One of the first things I noticed, during my first week in Sun Park, was that the whole resort - the entire complex - had been built around mutual and unwavering trust. Trust is the default setting. The bag is full of marbles from the moment you walk through the main gate. I remember the first day, I was at the cafe and hadn't had a chance to get cash from the bank. "No worries." said Eddie, who looked after the cafe. "Settle up next time."

Starting from a position of trust was quite a paradigm shift for me. I'd worked in a company for decades but was required to show a doctor's note if I had more than one day off sick. That meant having to take more time off work to visit the doctor's surgery, and paying £30 for a 'sick note'. What a waste of my money and the doctor's time!

In the early years, I had to fill in timesheets at work. This wasn't done to bill clients because my role didn't directly relate to individual clients. My timesheets were designed solely to monitor what I was doing with my time at work. In recent years, timesheets had been abandoned because all activity was logged via the workstation computers.

The company's distrust of its employees went further. Staff were not allowed to discuss matters of pay with other colleagues, new policies and procedures were decided in secret, without consultation, behind closed doors. The staff were informed by email of any new rule or regulation.

This culture of mistrust by our employer extended to the employees too. My co-workers didn't just distrust management, they didn't trust each other. If someone left their workstation, even for a few minutes, they would usually lock their drawers and password protect their computers. Even though we were work colleagues and, some - like me - had worked together for decades; and even though nobody, other than co-workers, had access to the office in which we all worked, nobody would leave anything of value in their coat pockets when they hung up their coat in the cloakroom.

The truth of the matter is that trust is not high on the agenda in most offices. It's not high on the agenda in most places. Perhaps we've all been conditioned to distrust everyone until they've filled our bag with enough marbles.

One evening, I was chatting with Greg on the main terrace. It was quite late in the afternoon, sometime after 5pm. I was walking back to my apartment from the Marigold and noticed Greg sitting with another guest, Terry, an artist from Swindon. Greg introduced Terry and I. "Terry did the magnificent mural in the Marigold", Greg said.

"That's impressive." I said. "Quite a piece of art."

"Thanks." said Terry. "It still needs some finishing touches, but I think it livens the place up a bit."

"Of course." interjected Greg. Turning to me, Greg asked how I was enjoying my stay so far.

"I'm loving it." I said. "I'm curious about one thing though."

"Shoot." said Greg.

"How did the idea of the honesty boxes evolve?"

"Ah..." said Greg. "Well, we believe that just as trust is an essential for happiness, it is equally important for a business. People are a lot happier and more productive when they know they can trust the people around them. Did you know that surveys in the UK and USA revealed that levels of trust have fallen from 60% to 30% in the past fifty years?"

"I'm not surprised." I said.

"Building a culture of trust is what makes a meaningful difference to our lives," said Greg. "Psychologists have demonstrated that, in the workplace, a trusting environment leads to 74% less stress, 106% more energy at work, 50% higher productivity, 13% fewer sick days, 76% more personal engagement, 40% less burnout and - as a result of all this - people experience 29% more satisfaction with their lives.

"So, transfer those findings to our lives outside the workplace and you've got yourself less stress, more energy, better health, improved relationships and greater satisfaction in your life. All through an attitude of trust."

I hadn't heard of this before, but it kind of made sense.

"And, let's look at sales and marketing," Greg continued. "Would you buy a product or service from a company or person if you didn't trust them?"

"No, probably not." I agreed.

"It's sales and marketing 101" Greg smiled. "We all want to buy from people or organisations we know, like and trust."

"That's true." I said. "I've heard that many times."

"Without trust," continued Greg, "business stops, and the economy stops. Without trust, society would fall into chaos. The simple fact is that the more distrustful we become, the more insular, isolated and miserable we become, and that can't be good.

"That's why everything at Sun Park is based upon complete trust." Greg opened his arms gesturing to everything in front of him. "As you can see, most of the on-site services have no cashier or till. All of the products are available to anyone to just go and take whatever they need or want, and we trust them to put the money in the honesty box. This situation doesn't exist in many places in the world.

"Trust is actually a prerequisite for our happiness." Greg said. "If you don't trust anyone, you'll never be happy." Greg took a breath. The issue of trust, like many aspects of the ethos, was something he was very passionate about. "Psychologists have demonstrated that trust is actually the biggest factor in determining our happiness. It's more important than our income and it's more important even than our health. That's why we value trust so much at Sun Park."

Then he said, "Look around you, Stan. What do you see?"

I looked below at the gardens and pool area. There were people on sunbeds by the pool. Other people were sitting around tables and chairs on the terrace, chatting and drinking tea and coffee.

"Really look." Greg said, aware that I wasn't noticing what he was trying to point out.

I looked beyond the gardens and the swimming pools to the apartment blocks, but still nothing really stood out.

"Come" said Greg, standing up. "Let's walk. It'll come to you."

We walked down the stairs, across the pool area to the facing apartment block. We walked down the pathway beside the ground floor apartments. Most doors were wide open. We stopped at one. "Hello!" called Greg through one apartment door. He smiled and did the same with the neighbouring apartment. Still, no reply.

"You see?" said Greg. "Where else would you find people happy to leave their doors wide open even when they're not at home?"

He had me there. I didn't know of anybody back home who would leave their front door unlocked, let alone wide open, if they weren't at home.

"Knowing that you're safe and your possessions are secure any time of the day or night is very...liberating." he said. "People here don't feel constantly worried or threatened. In fact, nowhere else gives you the same feeling of safety and security."

When we got to the next apartment, the door was shut, but there was a Kindle on the table outside. Greg knocked on the door and called "Hello! Anybody home?". This time someone was home. An attractive woman with long, blonde hair and large, bright blue eyes came to the door.

"Hello, Greg." she said smiling. The woman was slim, around 5'5" tall, with a smooth, tanned complexion and she was wearing white shorts and a dark blue sports vest. This was a woman who clearly could make heads turn but, more than that, such was her vibrancy, she could light up any room she entered.

Greg gave her a hug and introduced me.

"We were just passing by," he said.

"Perfect timing. I was just putting the kettle on. Can I get you both a drink?".

"Water would be lovely." said Greg.

"Oh, I can do better than that." she said. "How about a tea? I've got black tea, green tea, herbal tea, lemon and ginger..."

"Oh, okay. Green tea would be great."

"Green tea it is." she said, then turning to me, "How about you Stan?"

"Green tea sounds great to me too." I said. "Thank you."

Greg and I sat down at the table on the terrace and a few minutes later this wonder woman reappeared with a tea pot, glass mugs and a plate of assorted biscuits.

The woman's name was Paula and she was from Ellesmere Port in Cheshire. Sun Park was now her home. She had been there for two years, living with her dog, Alfie, an Affenpinscher, a terrier breed, small, feisty, and very friendly dog.

"Stan arrived a few days ago for a couple of weeks." Greg said.

"How do you like it?" asked Paula.

"It's quite amazing." I said. "I can see why you'd want to live here."

"Tell Stan your story." Greg said to Paula.

"There really isn't much to tell," she said. "I was diagnosed with Multiple Sclerosis three years ago."

"I'm sorry." I said. It was difficult to believe looking at how healthy Paula seemed. "You look the picture of health to me."

She smiled. "Thank you. I feel healthy here. In the UK though, I was a different woman. I had a busy life and I was constantly tired. I thought nothing of it, we all get fatigued from time to time, don't we?"

I nodded. There were plenty of days when I felt exhausted.

"Then one day, I noticed a numbness in my lower legs and then tingling sensations going up my arms. I went to my GP and a week later, after hospital tests, I was told that I had MS.

"Much as I love my hometown, I decided that I'd be better off in a warmer climate. I found Sun Park online and came out, just for a week, to see what it was like."

"By yourself?"

"Yes, and I must say that I was a bit nervous, but my fears were quickly dispelled. It just felt so safe and secure, plus everyone was very friendly. After the fourth day, I decided to extend my stay for a month. That month turned into two, and here I am. Of course, I go home now and again, to see family and friends, but I'm here with Alfie most of the time."

"What about your husband?" I asked.

"Oh, for the first year he came out whenever he could. He couldn't come out to live full-time due to his work, but he was able to come regularly, and he could see I was safe. I think the biggest thing was he could see that my symptoms had improved so much. Now, he's here with me all the time and loves it as much as I do."

"So, your health is that much better for being here?" I asked.

"It's amazing." said Paula. "Like night and day! MS is an autoimmune disease. They still don't fully understand what triggers it. But, I think, like all autoimmune diseases stress and diet and lifestyle all play a part."

I nodded. I knew from my own health, having had Psoriasis most of my life - which was also an autoimmune disease - that stress could trigger flare ups and I had read that streptococcal throat infections often preceded acute inflammation. I knew that less stress, the fresh sea air, sunshine and the vitamin D it delivers, fresh fruits and vegetables, these things make a difference.

I thought Paula's eyes welled up very slightly as she continued, "I believe that being here has...you'll think this silly...in a way, it has saved my life."

Greg touched Paula's shoulder. Alfie raised his head and, with eyes fixed on Paula, placed his front right paw on her foot. Paula stroked his head.

"It's interesting," she said, "I really don't think my improved health is down to any one factor. Yes, the sunshine and warm weather is rejuvenating, the fresh air, the exercise...but I think there's much more to it. Had I been somewhere else on this island, sitting alone in a villa, I don't think I'd be feeling as strong or healthy because I wouldn't have been as happy. I stay here, at Sun Park, because of the people. I've got wonderful friends here. People I can rely on. People who will always be there for me. As corny as it sounds, I stay here for the love. That's what Sun Park means to me. That's the essence of the ethos.

CHAPTER 13: A DAY OUT

*'The desire to share is not a vague, windy sentiment,
not when you see the massive rise in live concerts in
response to the phenomenon of downloading music...
People want to get rid of the headphones and be part
of a shared experience.'*
Richard Eyre

Tuesday morning. 9:30am. I was on a coach with
forty-seven other people heading to one of the
island's main tourist attractions on the other side of
the island. Truth be told, I've always tried to avoid
coach trips and organised group tours in the past,
mainly because I don't travel well on buses or boats.
But, I had been assured that our destination was only
a little over an hour away and Jeannie had said that
where we were going was something totally unique
to the island which shouldn't be missed.

I sat at the back of the bus, next to the window,
reasoning that I'd have less chance of feeling
nauseous if I could see out of the window. Next to me
were Kirsty, Krystal, and Jim and Pippa's sister,
Alison. Shortly after we set off, Jacob took the
microphone and invited volunteers to participate in
Coach Karaoke. Sheets of paper with lists of song
titles were passed around. Participation was
optional, and those who did want to take the
microphone could choose to sing alone or with a
partner. I'm not a big fan of Karaoke, partly because
I can't sing and partly because I've never got over a
childhood trauma when, as a child of four years old,
whilst singing *I'm A Little Teapot* on a family holiday,

I suddenly became very self-conscious, stopped mid-song and ran crying into my mother's arms. But on this journey, everyone got into the spirit of the occasion and I have to say that it was a lot of fun. Some of the older among us chose songs from the sixties, 'Summer Holiday' by Cliff Richard, 'My Guy' by Mary Wells, and then, of course, came the Beatles. Denny's rendition of 'Hey Jude' went down a storm. Kirsty and Krystal had the crowd throwing their arms in the air with 'It's Raining Men'. The whole coach was buzzing.

We travelled north through the island's capital, Arrecife, and up winding mountain roads to the north-east coast of the island. The terrain became greener and richer in foliage the further north we travelled, and the views out to the coast were, at times, breath-taking. I was chatting with Kirsty and Krystal when the coach stopped. I looked at my watch; it had been almost exactly an hour from the time I had stepped on the coach to the moment I stepped off. We were all standing in a car park on the top of a cliff, the Atlantic Ocean, sparkling in the sunshine, stretched out before us. We were about to enter one of the island's favourite tourist attractions, the place that the legendary Hollywood movie star, Rita Hayworth, described as 'the eighth wonder of the world', Jameos del Agua.

The Jameos del Agua are part of a long lava tube, over six kilometres in length, formed over 4,000 years ago when one of the island's volcanoes, Montaña La Corona, erupted. The molten lava created vast channels which hardened over decades forming tubes which ran down under the rock and into the Atlantic. Today the Jameos is an oasis like no other I have seen.

On entering the Jameos, you climb down a stone-staircase into the first cave which is known as 'Jameo Chico' (the little opening). This is home to an unusual cafe come restaurant, with views over a small, natural lake. The water is continually being refreshed by the Atlantic Ocean. You can see straight through, as if looking through crystal and, when you look closely, you can see the 'Jameios', a species of blind albino crabs, no bigger than a thumbnail. This is the only place on Earth that these creatures can be found.

Moving across the lake via a narrow footpath you enter the 'Jameo Grande', a turquoise pool of water that tantalises and teases on a hot summer's day as swimming is strictly prohibited. At the far end is a magnificent auditorium carved into the rock but largely the result of the volcanic eruption centuries earlier. You can imagine no better venue for a concert. This is Nature's cathedral, unparalleled beauty combined with mesmerising acoustics. The Jameo Grande is, quite literally, awe-inspiring.

Outside the Jameo Grande is a museum that explains the formation and history of the site, the volcanic eruptions over the centuries that simultaneously decimated old landscapes and gave birth to new ones. The site itself was the brainchild of César Manrique, an artist and architect who, native to the island, was highly respected and revered by the locals for his work protecting the island from predatory tourism. It is due in no small part to

Manrique's efforts that you won't see high rise hotels marring the Lanzarote coastlines.

By 1:30pm all the group had congregated for drinks at the cafe overlooking the pool. There was a lunch menu, but eating there was not part of the excursion. Instead Jacob had arranged for us to eat elsewhere. "It's beautiful," he said, "trust me!".

Fifteen minutes later we were sitting in a charming family-owned restaurant in a small mountain village overlooking green pastures in the valley below. The restaurant itself was basic both in decor and menu. However, the food was fresh and plentiful, and the meal was exceptional value. We sat together on long benches and enjoyed a leisurely Spanish lunch from an all-you-can-eat buffet. The restaurant overlooked the valley below where shepherds tended to flocks of sheep in the mountain fields.

At the end of the meal, I stood outside and looked up the main street. The location was stunning. It was as if we had travelled back in time to the last century. The street was cobbled, and the locals sat outside their homes, smoking and drinking coffee. The village shops were closed during the afternoon siesta, only the gift shop next to the restaurant remained open for business.

Ten minutes later, after people had had a chance to look at the local wares and buy some memorabilia, we were on our way back to Sun Park. As we journeyed down the mountains, I reflected on the day. Witnessing the Eighth Wonder of the World was a memorable experience, but I couldn't help wondering how different the experience would have been had I gone on my own or with a group of strangers. I don't think experiences of discovery or adventures made alone are ever as complete as those shared with friends.

We arrived back at Sun Park forty-five minutes later. Jacob thanked everyone for coming. As I got off the coach, Jacob was waiting. I moved to shake his hand. Instead of taking my hand, he opened his arms and gave me a hug. "Thanks so much for coming, Stan. I hope you enjoyed the day." he said.

"Jacob! The thanks are all mine. I wouldn't have missed it for the world!".

Chapter 14: Just For Today

'What we are today comes from our thoughts of yesterday, and our present thoughts build our life of tomorrow. Our life is the creation of our mind.'
Buddha

"You're here now and that's all that matters." Greg's words echoed in my head throughout my first week at Sun Park. There are times when my mind turned to thoughts of the future; the trip would be at an end soon, what would I do when I went back? I didn't have enough put by to be able to retire, and I had no idea what I was going to do.

One morning I confided in Greg. "Stan" he said, "You're here now and that's all that matters."

"Yes, but..."

"Stan," interrupted Greg, "just for today don't allow your fears to rob you of this moment, because the moment is all that we have."

Of course, I'd heard and been given that kind of advice many times in the past. Focus on the present moment. Don't dwell on the past or worry about the future. For me, that's much easier said than done. That said, one thing I did appreciate, after having spent some time at Sun Park and meeting some amazing people, is that, when worries surface, it helps to have a supportive network of friends around you.

"Why just for today?" I asked.

"Because today, right now, is all we have, and it's all that matters. There are many people here – and elsewhere - that have a lot more to worry about than you and I." he said. "I'm sure you've met some people here who have suffered terrible tragedies and loss in the past, and there are others who have to battle with disability and serious, chronic health problems. We are all facing very uncertain futures. None of us knows what the future has in store. So, we say 'just for today'. Any further is merely presumption. What counts is right here and now. We remember the past and we make plans for the future, but we live in the moment. You know the famous quote by Mark Twain?"

I had no idea, and shook my head.

"He said, *'I have known a great many troubles in my life, but most of them never happened.'*

I smiled. How true! Many things I had worried about over the years had never amounted to anything. There had been some things that had caused me a lot of anguish but, most of the time, catastrophe had somehow been avoided. I had survived. Perhaps I need to remind myself of that more often.

"Whenever you feel overwhelmed," Greg said, "tell yourself, 'Just for today I am fine.' Or 'Just for today, I will cope' or 'Just for today, I'll be thankful.' Just for today, enjoy what you have. Imagine you've decided you want to lose weight. You might decide to go on a restrictive diet, or on a fitness or exercise regime. It can be overwhelming to think of weeks and weeks, perhaps months of dieting and exercise, but if we take each day as it comes, it becomes manageable.

"I'm not religious at all, but all of the scriptures say the same thing: 'give us *this* day our daily bread'. Not give us our daily bread tomorrow or next week. Similarly, all the twelve step programs for people who are addicted to alcohol, or drugs or gambling, whatever...they all recommend one step at a time, one day at a time. It isn't just therapy for addiction, it is a prescription for living a full and happy life. That's why it's part of the ethos."

"Just for today..." I repeated. "I think that I'm going to try it. Can I ask you, what you do? Do you ever feel overwhelmed?"

Greg touched my shoulder. "The only place you'll find people who are never overwhelmed or stressed is in a cemetery." he said. "I do have one secret to share though.

"I learned it years ago from a friend," Greg said. "He came across a phone booth in the desert that had a sign saying, 'Talk to God'."

I smiled. "No, really," said Greg. "True story! I've seen the pictures. Have you ever heard of the Burning Man?"

"No, I can't say I have." I said. "I don't think I've ever come across him."

"That's because it's not a 'him', it's a festival. Every year in Black Rock City, Colorado, over fifty thousand people converge in this man-made city in the desert for eight days and nights for what is described as a festival of radical self-expression. Here, I'll show you…"

Greg opened his smartphone and showed me some photos. "My friend took these." he said.

It looked like a massive adult playground. There were huge sculptures, incredible esoteric light shows and concerts. People were dancing, singing, chanting, attending workshops, group meditation, yoga. I'd never seen anything like it.

"They refer to it as a culture of possibility. Or, a network of dreamers and doers." Greg said. "Here's the phone booth." Sure enough, there was a photo of a phone booth with a sign saying, 'Speak to God'.

"My friend was walking around the city when he came across the phone booth. So, he thinks to himself, 'How often do you get the chance to speak through a direct phone line to God?' and he decides to go into the phone booth and make a call.

"To his surprise, a soft voice answers and asks what he could do for my friend. My friend had one question, 'How can I live more in the moment?'. He was aware that some of the most beautiful moments of his life had been lost to anxiety. There were many times when he had been fixated on regrets from the past, and worries about the future. We all have them. But, my friend was a worrier by nature. Hard as he tried, the anxieties would take hold. He wanted to know how someone like him could cope better whenever those fears and anxieties arose. And, to his utter amazement, God answered him with one word... 'Breathe'.

"At first, the advice seemed trite. After all, we hear it so often, don't we? When we're in pain or suffering from an anxiety attack, or even an asthma attack, a friend or therapist will say 'Breathe'. When a woman gives birth, she is told the same thing, 'Breathe'."

I knew that breathing is often recommended to help people manage pain and alleviate anxiety. For some reason though, I had never really tried it. Maybe, when there's no direct phone line, God speaks through the people around us?

"My friend reasoned that if God speaks, perhaps he should listen." Greg said. "So, when he got home, whenever he would start to feel anxious about anything - whether it was related to his future or his past - he would remember to breathe. Deep breaths, in and out. He would concentrate on his breath, inhaling and exhaling; slowly and deliberately. Breathe in, breathe out."

"And did it work?".

"Of course. It works every time, without fail." Greg said. "Anxiety subsides almost instantly, and you can literally feel yourself relaxing."

"Well it sounds easy enough." I said.

"It is simple, yes" Greg said, "but not easy. That's why it is useful to learn to meditate too."

"Really?" I said. "Doesn't that take years to learn?"

"Not at all." said Greg. "You can learn it and practise it within minutes. You should go along to the meditation classes. You'll find the times on the noticeboard."

I promised to check it out. "Please do." said Greg. "I'll be interested to hear how you get on."

~

The following morning, I attended a meditation class run by Martin Rush. An ironic surname for a man who teaches meditation. Martin has a shaved, bald head and a trimmed, white goatee beard without which I'd have guessed him to be somewhere in his fifties rather than his actual age which was seventy.

I had never tried any form of meditation in the past, and had Greg not been so effusive in his praise for meditation, I would have probably given it a miss, simply because there were so many other activities I wanted to try. Pétanque, Bridge, Cycling and Hiking were all on my to-do list.

There were twelve people, including Martin, at the class. We sat on upright garden chairs arranged in a circle. Martin began the session by explaining a little about what meditation was and what we could expect.

"There is nothing complicated about meditation." he said. "It's just a technique that enables you to be an observer of your thoughts and feelings." Apparently, we have between 50,000-70,000 thoughts every day, which means we're having between 35 and 48 thoughts per minute. "This is what psychologists refer to as 'mind chatter' and this constant chattering can be exhausting and very stressful."

In the past few years, there had been times when I'd noticed myself talking to myself. I would be alone in my house and I would catch myself speaking my thoughts aloud. Martin explained that this wasn't, as we so often hear, the first sign of insanity. In fact, Martin said, it was a sign of sanity. Apparently, everybody has these conversations with themselves, all day, every day. Sometimes, we just verbalise those thoughts. I smiled, happy in the knowledge that I was not mad after all.

"Meditation allows you be an observer of all of your mind chatter" Martin said. "All your thoughts and feelings. Feelings are triggered by thoughts, but where do our thoughts come from? Do we choose our thoughts? Or, do our thoughts choose us?".

There was a momentary pause as Martin let us ponder the question. "Human beings are no different in this regard to the rest of the animal kingdom" he said. "In fact, you could say the same thing about everything in Nature... we are responsive or reactive beings. Everything we think, say or do, is a response to some external stimuli."

I had my doubts. Don't we human beings direct our own thoughts? If we didn't, we'd be no more than robots. Sensing our doubt, Martin gave the following example: an insect bites your leg, it stings or itches and you scratch it. Your hand touches a hot plate and without hesitation or thought, you pull your hand away. Or, you see an attractive member of the opposite sex and your pupils dilate. These are examples of what we'd call involuntary responses. You don't make these on a conscious level."

So far, so good. I could accept Martin's logic.

"Smell a freshly baked loaf of bread and you might start salivating. Hearing or even reading the word 'yawn' will cause many people to start yawning. These are uncontrolled physical reactions."

I yawned as he said it, as did most of the group. Yawns, I had to agree, are most definitely infectious.

"We are reactive beings." said Martin. "Our thoughts, our emotions, our biochemistry and physiology, all are affected by everything around us. "Words, sights, sounds, smells and touch; we react to them all. And, it all happens on a unconscious level. Advertisers rely on this fact. They associate products with positive emotions which usually means connecting a product with things people like. They'll show a Pepsi bottle with young people dancing and having a good time and the latest downloaded tune on iTunes might be playing in the background.

"What is wrong with this?" Martin said. "Nothing if you don't mind your thoughts being manipulated. But, if you want to live freely, you need to become aware of how your thoughts and emotions are being directed.

"Once you're aware of these issues, you can turn the tables and use the same techniques to manipulate and improve your life."

"How do you do that?" I asked.

"You change your environment. You read different books, watch different movies, associate with people who share your values. And this is where Meditation comes into its own. It can help free your mind of the constant chatter and you become more aware of yourself and everything around you. Let's try it, shall we?

"Okay. Is everyone sitting comfortably? Good...uncross your legs and put your hands on your knees, and close your eyes." Martin started to guide us through a short meditation. "There is no struggle." he said. "Just be aware first of your posture. Imagine your head is being gently lifted, your chest opens out and your entire back gently straightens. Your neck is straightening too. Notice how your body feels; your feet and ankles, your knees and then your hips and pelvis. Focus on your torso...then your shoulders and arms...and hands. Now, focus on your neck and face. Just be aware of all of the sensations."

It was an interesting exercise to focus my attention on different parts of my body.

"Feel the breeze on your skin," Martin continued, "notice the sounds around you."

I could hear the breeze, the rustling of leaves and then I noticed the birdsong and the hum of traffic in the distance.

"Notice the smells", Martin said. The aroma of the jasmine incense brought back memories of my honeymoon in Northern Cyprus over thirty years ago. Images of the hotel, my wife and I, the only guests in the hotel, lying by pool.

"Now turn your attention to your breath...Notice as you inhale and exhale. Feel the breath as it comes through your nose and down your trachea into your lungs. With each breath, you breathe more deeply and more freely. Feel your diaphragm extending as your chest opens."

Martin told us to keep focussing on our breath. Allowing our thoughts to come and go without judging or analysing them. Each time a thought comes into your head, we were to refocus our attention on our breath. "Don't force anything," he said. "Just let your breathing come naturally."

The session continued in much the same way, with Martin reminding us to let go of any thoughts that may pop into our heads and focus our attention on our breathing. Martin guided our focus to each part of our bodies, starting with the feet and going up to the neck and head, allowing all of the joints and soft tissues to relax. Each time, he returned the focus to our breath. Before we finished, Martin told us to be aware once more of our surroundings. The session finished and in what seemed to be a matter of minutes, but when I checked my watch, over half an hour had passed.

"How do you feel?" Martin asked. Everyone felt relaxed. I felt a sense of calm and, at the same time, energised. My mind was free of any anxiety. Martin explained that meditation is a path to mindfulness. It enables us to be more mindful of our thoughts and feelings, and our actions. "Without being mindful of who we are and where we want to go in life" he said, "we are like sailors trying to navigate the seas without a compass or a rudder. The sails flap in the wind, and we end up drifting, out of control.

"Mindfulness provides a sense of awareness that allows us to understand where we are, how we arrived at where we are, and how to start to live with intention."

I thought about Greg's friend who received the message from God. 'Breathe'. Meditation is a tool that uses breathing to free your mind and allow you to live in the present, appreciating the 'here and now'. It was certainly very relaxing.

When I got back to my room a half hour after the class, I found a Whatsapp message on my phone from Greg. "Hi Stan. Hope you enjoyed the meditation class. If you haven't met Jeremy, apartment 716, go and introduce yourself. He'll have some answers to your questions."

CHAPTER 15: CHASING DREAMS

'The greatest achievement was at first and for a time a dream. The oak sleeps in the acorn, the bird waits in the egg, and in the highest vision of the soul a waking angel stirs. Dreams are the seedlings of realities.'
James Allen

Jeremy Croxford was a few years my junior. I knocked on his door later that afternoon and explained that Greg had sent me. "Greg and I were talking earlier, and he said I should talk to you." I said.

Jeremy smiled. "Sure" he said, "come in". Jeremy's apartment was on the first floor and overlooked the pool area. He brought out some iced water and a bowl of nuts, and we sat on his terrace. It was a beautiful vista looking down on the swimming pools and gardens. The sun was still high in the sky, and the birds were chirping in the tops of the palm trees. "Fantastic, isn't it?" he said, raising his glass. "Salud!"

Jeremy was divorced and had three grown up children who were all living their own lives. He explained that he had owned a recruitment business in Manchester and was going about his life quite happily, or so he thought, until one day he received news that changed his life forever.

"All of my life I'd been focussed on succeeding in business. I read self-help books and watched motivational videos." he said. "I went to the seminars and workshops. You know the kind?"

I knew exactly what he meant. A guru or self-proclaimed expert stands up and talks and presents ideas using phrases that make you feel as if your chest is being pumped up and, for a few days at least, you feel like there's nothing you can't do.

"I heard all the motivational sayings like, Seize the day... Don't wait for your ship to come in, swim out to it...Tough times never last, tough people do...You always miss one hundred percent of the shots you don't take... If you can believe it, you can achieve it... Success is going from failure to failure without losing your enthusiasm ... If at first you don't succeed, try, try again... Success is one percent inspiration ninety-nine percent perspiration... If you don't know where you're going you will end up somewhere else... just do it!"

I nodded. I'd heard and read many of them too.

"But, here's the thing," said Jeremy, "There was one phrase that inspired and motivated me above all others, and it has kept me motivated every day since the moment I heard it. It wasn't something I read in a book and I didn't hear it at a seminar or workshop." Jeremy paused and leaned forward. "It was told to me by a man who probably didn't even realise the effect that his words would have on me."

I nodded, and leaned forward, eager to hear what this magic phrase was and who had told it to him.

"It was my doctor." said Jeremy. "I had been to see him because I had been feeling exhausted and suffering from recurring stomach cramps. He ordered some blood tests and then, in a very matter-of-fact way, my doctor said, 'Jeremy, you've got tumours on your liver.' I asked him what that meant and then he said the word we all dread... cancer. Worst still, it was untreatable. The best-case scenario? Two years.'"

I inhaled, not knowing what to say.

"I can tell you," Jeremy continued, "if those words don't motivate you, nothing will!"

I nodded. "I'm so sorry".

"Thank you, but don't be", Jeremy said. "That was seven years ago. It turns out that doctors are not clairvoyants, after all."

"So, what happened?" I asked. I'd never spoken to anyone who had faced death like that before.

"You know about the five stages of grief?" Jeremy said.

I shook my head. "Not really."

"Okay. So, psychologists claim that we when we suffer a significant loss, like someone close to us dies, or we suffer an accident and - I don't know - become paralysed, lose our sight or hearing...something that we had that we can't get back, we tend to go through five stages of grief...

"Stage one is denial. 'They're not dead.' or 'This isn't happening to me.' or 'I'm not dying'. But, sooner or later, the truth becomes unavoidable, and then comes stage two which is anger; Life is unfair! Why me? To hell with everyone. To hell with the world!' This, we all know, gets us nowhere.

"And then, the third stage, anger turns to bargaining. Now we might plead with God or some Higher Power, 'Help me and I promise I'll be a good boy, or girl', as if our suffering was some sort of punishment from a petty minded, vindictive deity!

"Sooner or later, we realise that, despite what the holy scriptures would have us believe, God can't be bargained with, and so we enter the fourth stage...depression. The hopelessness of our predicament weighs down on us like a ten-ton truck. We struggle to get free and continue to struggle, all the time getting nowhere, until we reach the fifth and final stage which is... acceptance.

"This is the point where, finally, we feel free. We realise that we can't change what has happened and we begin to realise that our suffering has come with a gift."

"Really?" I said. I found it very hard to believe that any form of loss or suffering could be thought of as a gift.

"When we reach the stage of acceptance," said Jeremy, "we come to the realisation that we have one final freedom which is this: whilst we might not be able to change our situation, we can change ourselves, or more specifically, we can change how we respond to the situation."

I leaned back and took a deep breath, not really appreciating what Jeremy was saying. "Hmm. I'm not sure I fully understand." I said. "I mean how did you 'change your response'?

Jeremy smiled. "Good question. I had been given a death sentence. The time I had left was finite. Two years. What could I do? What should I do?"

"So, what did you do?" I interrupted.

"Before I answer that, let me ask you, what would you do?"

I thought a moment. "You know, to be honest, Jeremy, I've never really thought about it before. What would I do if I knew I had two years to live?"

"Yes. Let's imagine you've just learned that you've got a maximum of twenty-four months left to live. What now? It's a tough one, right?" Jeremy said.

I shook my head. At that moment, I couldn't think of anything.

"I didn't know either, at first." said Jeremy. "Then it came to me... Once you know that your time here is limited, you want to make whatever you have left really count, right?"

I nodded. "You're absolutely right." I said. It was a good answer. If you only had a few years to live, you'd want to make the most of every day.

"So, what would you do?" Jeremy asked.

I took a long breath and looked around. There were groups of people sunbathing by the pool. It was a beautiful day. A perfect day. Bright sunshine cooled by a gentle sea breeze. Ruddy shell ducks flew in a vee formation overhead. People were chatting around tables on the terrace nearby. And, laughter was coming from the art studio downstairs. What was I missing? I just didn't have an answer.

"Don't worry." Jeremy said. "Most people struggle with that question. But, here's the thing... we're all dying. We just don't know when it will be. It could be tomorrow. Or next week. It might be next year, or it could be decades away. But one thing is certain, it is going to come to all of us. We just don't want to think about it."

Of course, Jeremy was right. I was sixty years of age and I knew that I was not going to live forever. I just didn't know when my time would be up and, to be frank, I didn't want to know.

Jeremy continued, "A friend of a friend recommended Sun Park. I looked it up on the internet and, I thought to myself, 'I've got limited time, but this sounds worth investing some of that time.' The chance to try new experiences, make new friends, be part of something. It all resonated with me and while I was here, something unexpected happened...the answer came to me.

"I was sitting in one of the workshops in the Learning Annex. It was about the power of journaling."

I made a mental note to see if the workshop was still available during my stay.

"One of the things that came up" Jeremy continued, "was how, in most situations, nobody can give you better advice for your life than you can. When you think about it, nobody knows you or your life experiences, or your thoughts and feelings, and your goals and aspirations, better than you do."

I nodded. "But don't you think that sometimes we can be too close to our own issues to see things as clearly as someone else?"

"That's where journaling comes into play." said Jeremy. "Many psychologists believe that we need to learn to trust ourselves more. You know what I mean? Go with your gut."

I thought about that for a second. I had been made redundant less than six weeks ago. I had limited savings, no pension to speak of, no idea of what I was going to do in the future and yet, I had chosen to come out to Lanzarote to a place I knew very little about and be among people I didn't know. To an observer, it might not make much sense. I could easily see why some people would think it illogical. Yet, something inside me told me it was the right thing to do. And, the more time I spent here, the more I felt that it had been the right decision. I had no proof, of course. Time would tell, but I had gone with my gut.

Looking back at my life, I can remember many times when I went against my instinct and instead chose whatever seemed like the logical thing to do. Who knows what's right or wrong? I guess we'll never know. One thing I did know; even the limited experience I had had at Sun Park was enough for me to appreciate that, during my stay, I had changed. My life was changing every day.

"Anyway, I was sitting in the workshop" continued Jeremy, "and, at one point, we're all writing down our goals. And, I'm thinking about the things I wanted to do in the limited time I've got left. Incredible as it may sound, I've never actually sat down and done that before. You know what I mean? As crazy as it sounds, I've never consciously sat down and thought about all of the things I wanted to do in my life."

Hearing Jeremy say that made me think about what I wanted to do with my life. I had never written out any kind of goals in my life before. Yes, I'd written down New Year's resolutions a few times, but those were usually forgotten about before the end of January. And, if I'm honest, I'd reasoned years ago that, at my time in life, there's not much point in setting out goals.

"I sat staring at a blank piece of paper for a while" continued Jeremy, "and then something came to me...I was going to write a book. I know, everyone says that they want to write a book, but then again, how many actually do? We put it off. Like everything else. We file it in the 'someday' cabinet. But, I couldn't do that. I had no 'somedays' left. It was either now or never.

"Quite a few years ago, I'd had an idea for a book but, like I said, I never got around to writing it. There were always so many distractions and, like many people, what time I did have, I spent doing other things.

"The difference was that now I had a deadline. I had two years to write my book and get it published. There and then, I decided that I was going to focus my attention back on that dream. I was going to do whatever it took to finish that book, and I brought the deadline to finish it forward by a year. One year to write it, and the next to get it published.

"Wasting no time, I read the top ten best-selling books in the same genre that my book was intended for. Those books had around two hundred pages. With an average of around four hundred words on a page, I was going to need to write 70-80,000 words. So, I prepared a synopsis and chapter outline, and I made a commitment to myself to write five hundred words every day. That meant my book should be finished - at least in draft form - within 140-160 days. That seemed doable to me. It wouldn't even take six months."

"It sounds simple", I said, "But I'm sure it's not."

"Simple, it is. But, easy it isn't." said Jeremy. "However, something happened during that time...I stopped dying."

"Really?" I said astonished.

"Well, not exactly. As I said, we're all dying. But, it dawned on me that, for one of the first times in my life, my focus was on living.

"Here's the secret," he continued, "anybody who has ever chased a dream will know that it lights a fire inside you. It doesn't even matter whether you achieve the dream or not. Once that fire has been ignited, you feel ...energised. I mean, you don't roll out of bed, you jump out, excited for the day ahead!"

I tried to think back to a time when I last jumped out of bed, or looked forward excitedly to the day ahead. The last time was the morning I came to Sun Park on a Social Friday. I was genuinely excited that morning. But, before that? I really couldn't tell you.

"You know what the definition of success is, Stan?" Jeremy continued.

"Erm, I suppose achieving a goal?" I said.

"That's one definition." Jeremy replied. "But pure success was best defined by the great American writer, Earl Nightingale. He said that success is 'the progressive realisation of a worthy ideal'."

"I like it!" I said. And, I meant it. *The progressive realisation of a worthy ideal.* What was my worthy ideal? I had no idea. But, before I could give it much thought, Jeremy continued, "When you're told your time is limited, you realise that you can't wait for your dreams to come to you. You have to work for them, and keep moving toward them."

I don't know why, but at that moment a memory resurfaced in my head. I was a young boy, eleven or twelve years old and I had been mesmerised by a series of sculptures depicting men, women and children coming out of different structures; in one they were walking out of a brick wall, another showed children running out of a tree, and there was one even more spectacular scene showing the globe with arms coming out of various countries with hands reaching towards and, in some cases, touching or holding the hands of other countries. I can't explain what it was about them at the time, but they were magical and all I wanted at that time was to create my own sculptures.

"Why do you think people stop chasing their dreams?" I asked.

"Here's my theory", he said. "We're all taught that life is tough... life's a bitch... life is hard. But, for many of us, life isn't hard at all. In fact, it's pretty easy."

"In what way?" I asked.

"It's pretty easy to sail through life" Jeremy said. "Most of us go to sleep and wake up every day with a roof over our heads, having slept in a comfy bed. Our fridges are full of food. I mean, yes, there are many, many people who are homeless and hungry, but most people in the West never have to worry about starvation or homelessness. Most of us have friends and family who will help us out if needed.

"It's pretty easy to grow up, put your dreams aside, leave your passions behind, take a job, raise a family - who will most likely do the exact same thing and follow the same path we took from point A to point B to Point C - until we all end up at point Z, which is where we leave the party. For most people, living really is pretty easy. But, living an inspiring life, having the courage to pursue your dreams, that is hard."

Of course, Jeremy was right. I knew it. I'd always known it. But, just as he said, I had been too busy going from point B to C to stop and really think about what I really wanted, or where I my life was headed.

"Pursuing your dreams is a key part of the ethos here at Sun Park," said Jeremy. "Everyone is encouraged to try new things, to learn and to pursue their own happiness in their own way. And, everyone supports one another.

"Ask yourself this: what are you dying to do? What is that worthy ideal you want to work towards? You'll find that nobody is going to shake their head at you or put you down by saying things like 'You're too old!' Or, you'll never do that!'. Everyone is genuinely rooting for you, and that means something.

"The ethos for me is about re-discovering your life's purpose, finding a dream that creates a spark inside you because, with persistence, that spark will become a flame and the flame will turn into a fire. And before you know it, you will have ignited a spark in those around you too.

"We all need to constantly remind ourselves that we're dying, and discover something that we're dying to do, because the minute we forget it - the moment we take life for granted - is the moment we stop living.

Jeremy was making complete sense now. How I wished, right then, that someone had told me this years ago.

"And here's the exciting part," said Jeremy. "The moment you start to live your dreams, you stop dying and start living. I was very lucky. My doctor's words could have ended my life. I could have given up and prepared for the inevitable. But, I came here and started to dream again, which is to live again and, for whatever reason and despite the damning prognosis, my tumours didn't grow. I stayed healthy."

"That is amazing!" I said.

"It really is," Jeremy said. "Dreaming and living your dreams is central to the ethos here. You'll be pushed to find anyone who doesn't pursue a dream. Now, it might not be a grand dream that's going to change the world. A dream could be as simple as acquiring a new skill, learning a new language, playing a musical instrument, or even completing a painting. The secret is to find something, and do it!

"So, this is the challenge everyone needs to face." said Jeremy. "It is very simple: ask yourself 'What am I dying to do?'. Don't go to sleep tonight without answering that question because there's nothing more important than figuring that out. And, when you do figure it out...well, then when you go to sleep, you'll find that - just as you did when you were a child - you'll be going to sleep not *to* dream but *with* a dream, and you'll wake up with one!"

I can't deny that Jeremy's story was inspiring. Maybe it wasn't too late for me to pursue some dreams of my own. Perhaps I could create sculptures like the ones I'd fallen in love with all those years ago. Was there still time to get a black belt in Aikido? Or learn a second language? Who said that somebody my age can't learn to play the guitar? These were things I had buried inside me decades ago, long before I got married. Talking with Jeremy had brought them back.

I had a lot to think about. I didn't know what I was going to do, and I still faced the same uncertain future. However, talking to Jeremy had given me a sense of optimism and hope. I was eager to get back to my apartment and start thinking about what dream I was going to chase in whatever time I had left.

CHAPTER 16: THE GREEN KITCHEN

*'If we are creating ourselves all the time, then it is
never too late to begin creating the bodies we want
instead of the ones we mistakenly assume
we are stuck with.'*
Deepak Chopra

During my short time at Sun Park I had met so many
amazing people, many of whom had made me re-
evaluate my beliefs and re-think aspects of my life.
One person who particularly inspired me and
challenged my beliefs was Shirley, a seventy-four-
year-old woman from Crawley, Sussex who had
been the driving force behind the creation of the
Green Kitchen.

Four days a week, people would gather in what was
the original kitchen and dining area of the restaurant
when Sun Park had been a traditional family holiday
resort. This covered a vast area which could easily
sit over two hundred people. For the first few years
the area had been left unused, largely because it
wasn't seen to be needed. Everyone had their
kitchenettes in their apartments and, until Shirley
arrived, nobody had thought it worthwhile to
reclaim the entire restaurant.

The idea behind the Green Kitchen was twofold: it
was to serve as a place where people could meet
and cook meals together rather than sit eating alone
in their apartments, and it was a facility whereby
members and guests could learn about plant-based
cookery, which is to say preparing vegetarian

meals. There was no meat, poultry or fish, and even dairy foods and eggs were excluded.

"Initially, quite a few people thought it was extreme not to eat animal products. Most people had grown up thinking that a meal wasn't complete unless it contained some form of meat and two veg." said Shirley. "But I guess that when people heard my story, they were more open to the idea."

Shirley's story was quite remarkable. She had been fit and active most of her life, specialising in long distance running which she continued well into her late forties. Then came a bombshell. She noticed lumps on the lateral section of her left breast and tests revealed that she had stage four breast cancer. Shirley's oncologist recommended a double mastectomy followed by a course of chemotherapy. Naturally, Shirley was devastated but she insisted on seeking a second opinion. She did her own research on the internet and found Dr John McDougall, who took a radically different approach to healthcare. Dr McDougall had successfully treated patients suffering from a range of cancers, heart disease and even type two diabetes using diet as therapy.

Shirley met with McDougall and reviewed his research which showed that meat, fish and dairy products were all closely associated with cancer, whereas plant-based foods, high in antioxidants and minerals, fought tumour growth. She followed McDougall's advice without compromise, and she also kept running. "I had never felt better," she said. "I made fresh juices every day and stuck to Dr McDougall's recipes. Tests three months later revealed the tumours had shrunk to less than half their size, and a further three months later I was cancer-free! They couldn't find any evidence of tumours anywhere."

"That is incredible." I said. "But tell me, what about fish? Isn't that supposed to be healthy?"

"Believe it or not," Shirley said, "Fish is more toxic than any other food."

"You're kidding." I said. "Isn't it full of Omega 3 essential fatty acids and protein?"

"The problem is that most fish is farmed and saturated with chemicals. Studies have shown that the chemical toxins are five times higher in farmed fish than any other food. You can look it up for yourself. The thing is, for me, I was in a critical situation. I knew that I either had to follow Dr McDougall's program or have my breasts removed."

"I must say that was very brave to go against the oncologist's advice."

"Not really," said Shirley. "I had a cancer specialist looking after me, but I didn't rely on his say-so, I looked at the research myself. My oncologist explained that the survival rate of women in my condition who underwent a mastectomy and chemotherapy was twenty-two percent. That is one in five women are alive after five years. So, if I'd have had my breasts removed and went through all of the side-effects that came with chemotherapy, I'd still only have a one-in-five chance of surviving five years!

"Dr McDougall's approach made sense to me and he had shown me the results his patients had had with his program. Ultimately, we all must make our own choices, but I felt more comfortable - no more optimistic - going with Dr McDougall. As I said, I looked at the research and made my decision. That doesn't mean to say that it would be the right decision for other people."

"Why not?"

"Well, you've got to be prepared to change your lifestyle, and many people aren't prepared to do that." she said. "Food can be like a drug. We get conditioned and, for some, they find the idea of change unthinkable. But, for me, it was an easy choice. As they say, 'Nothing tastes as good as being healthy and alive feels'!"

I thought about what Shirley was saying. I could appreciate the logic, but food was one of my few pleasures and there was no way that I would agree to giving up my favourite meals in the hope of living a few years longer. Sunday roasts, a rack of lamb with mint sauce and crispy roast potatoes, and simple fried, battered fish and chips made life worth living.

Shirley could see that I wasn't convinced. "Most people give me the same look, Stan, but at the same time, everybody wants to live a long full life, don't they?".

"Yes," I said, "but, with respect, it seems a bit extreme."

"What's more extreme," she asked, "having major surgery and bombarding your body with toxic chemicals and radiation, or changing your diet?"

"Point taken," I said, "but for people who are not in a critical condition, it seems like a radical diet to just eat plants."

"That is exactly why we started the Green Kitchen." she said. "People say the exact same thing, but that is only because they have no idea what plant-based foods are. Many people think that a plant-based diet is just eating rice, beans and salad. But, the truth is, every meal you currently eat can be made without meat. That's what the Green Kitchen is all about. We learn about the science behind healthy eating and, on the practical side, we learn how to make delicious meat-free meals. That includes things like burgers, mince, cutlets, schnitzels, even fishless fish burgers! You name it...all without meat."

I raised my eyebrows. "Yes, but they're not like the real thing, are they?"

"You'd be surprised, Stan." she said. "Come along sometime and judge for yourself."

The following day I went to The Green Kitchen. I had huge respect for Shirley. Not just because of how she had defeated cancer but, at the age of seventy-four, she still competed in 'Ironman Triathlons'. I was fourteen years her junior and I would have struggled to run a few hundred metres without collapsing in a heap. Shirley swam four kilometres, cycled one hundred and twenty kilometres and then ran an entire marathon - over twenty-six miles - all in one day in a single race! How can you not be impressed?

Just over thirty people turned up for the midday session. Shirley proceeded to give a talk about dairy food - milk and cheese. I've always been a big cheese lover; camembert, blue, stilton, brie - heaven! And, aside from being a bit high in fat, they're healthy. Rich in calcium and good for strong bones. Or so I thought.

Shirley explained that milk was a perfect food, but for calves and not humans. Far from strengthening bones and teeth, dairy foods have been shown to leach calcium from the bones. How? Milk and cheese change the body chemistry, they create acidity which the body then tries to correct by releasing calcium (which is alkaline) from the bones.

Studies had demonstrated that dairy consumption is associated with a significantly increased risk of bone fractures. In one twelve-year long study involving 77,761 women aged 34 through 59 years of age, researchers discovered that those women who consumed the most dairy foods broke more bones than those who rarely, if ever, drank milk. In addition, studies have shown that bone strength and density of people who *never* consumed dairy foods was significantly better than those who regularly consumed dairy foods.

Then Shirley brought out a range of alternative plant-based milks. These were made from nuts, rice, oats, or soya - all rich in calcium and vitamin D and low in fat. We tried them in tea and coffee, and

Shirley made strawberry and chocolate dairy-free milk shakes which, I had to admit, were delicious.

The rest of the session was spent making veggie burgers from scratch using black-eyed beans as the main ingredient along with onions, garlic, a range of herbs and spices including barbeque sauce, vegan Worcestershire sauce and soy sauce which were mixed and covered with breadcrumbs. I'm no cook, but it was actually a lot of fun and it was incredibly easy too. We mixed the ingredients, rolled the mixture into patties, and covered them in breadcrumbs. These were left to sit in the fridge for fifteen minutes before being baked in the oven for thirty-five minutes.

I was really surprised, not only at how simple the burgers were to make, but there was no denying that they were pretty damn good. To finish the meal off, we put our burgers inside a wholemeal bun with lettuce, tomato, a slice of gherkin, mild mustard and tomato ketchup and topped with a slice of diary-free cheese, and ate them with a cup of freshly cooked sweet potato fries. This was an entirely new experience for me - on a number of levels; after my wife had passed away, I had tended to live on ready-made meals, things that I could shove in the microwave or oven. I'd never cooked a meal like this from scratch, and I'd never eaten a meatless burger. But, more than that, I couldn't remember a time when I'd sat around tables with friends and eaten a meal that we'd all prepared together.

At the end of lunch, Shirley called me as the crowd began to disperse. Everyone helped clean and tidy up after the meal, but Shirley liked to check everything and ensure that nothing had been missed.

"What did you think?" she asked.

I held my hands up and told her how much I'd enjoyed the experience. I'd learned a lot too.

"That's what it's all about." smiled Shirley. "We all want to have new experiences and expose ourselves to new ideas."

"That's true." I said. "But this was quite something."

Over the years, the Green Kitchen became one of my favourite places in Sun Park. Shirley had initiated something that changed people's lives on a very practical and physical level. Researchers have discovered how and why plant-based foods improve our health; even at relatively advanced years the changes are evident. Cholesterol levels lower, blood sugar levels become stable, hardened plaque on artery walls dissolves and immunity markers in the blood improve.

One study conducted over a period of five years demonstrated that adhering to a plant-based diet reversed aging. How is it possible to grow younger as time passes? you might ask. I did. I googled it too, just to make sure it wasn't some made-up story.

In the study, scientists monitored people who ate a plant-base diet over five years and compared them biologically with a control group of people who ate a conventional diet which included meat, fish and dairy foods. Doctors know that, as we age, the ends of our chromosomes, known as telomeres, become shorter and shorter, and short telomeres are associated with age-related diseases. Every time a chromosome splits, the telomeres at its ends reduce in size. This is exactly what was seen in the control group. Everyone aged as the science had predicted. However, when the scientists reviewed the blood samples of the people who ate an exclusively plant-based diet, they were shocked by what they found: the telomeres had become longer. Typically, the telomeres in people who ate a plant-based diet increased by ten percent over the five-year period. The media pushes a narrative of youth through potions and lotions, and when that doesn't work, many resort to botox and surgery to hold on to youth, but the secret to staying biologically younger and healthier can be found in the food on your plate.

It was in the Green Kitchen that I learned about nutrition, how foods are also our most powerful medicines, and I learned how to cook with simple, natural ingredients. However, the highlight of my times in the Kitchen wasn't what I learned, it was the shared experience of cooking with friends and sharing our meals, because shared experiences - being together, learning together, and discovering together - tend to lead to very special bonds between people.

Everybody who attended the Green Kitchen loved the experience. Nobody ever left feeling hungry or lonely. I fell in love with it because it represented the very best of what Sun Park offered. It was fun, educational and, on many occasions, inspiring. It brought people together and meant that, for one meal every day, you really felt part of an extended family. It was like Sun Park itself; it doesn't matter how you might feel when you arrive, when it is time to leave, you feel inspired, even elated, and very thankful for the experience.

CHAPTER 17: THE GOOD LIFE

*'The good life is one inspired by love
and guided by knowledge.'*
Bertrand Russell

The Learning Annex is another one of my favourite places at Sun Park. It is, as the name suggests, a centre for learning, an auditorium where members and guests gather to listen to short talks and lectures, discuss ideas, and participate in workshops. It is where you come to learn and discover and discuss new ideas. A centre for personal growth or, as Greg likes to call it, a gymnasium for the mind and imagination.

The Learning Annex was originally inspired by the TED talks which are organised all over the world. At TED conferences, innovators, researchers, and educators share their experience and knowledge. TED is an acronym for Technology, Entertainment & Design and hosts events on a wide range of topics that fall within those three headings.

Initially, people congregated at the Learning Annex to watch recorded TED talks and these would typically be followed by an open discussion. However, over time, it became apparent that most people who stay at Sun Park had something to share.

Sun Park has a richness in diversity; people come from a wide variety of backgrounds; nurses, professors, researchers, scientists, lawyers, builders, dentists, entrepreneurs and even professional athletes were all represented. All it took was one person to offer to give a talk on his or her chosen field of expertise, and then others followed. People who had never spoken in public got the courage to stand up, and share their experience and knowledge before their peers.

Everyone is invited to share, regardless of background or qualifications. This is because, at the Learning Annex, it is acknowledged that everyone has something of interest and value to share; from health and wellness to psychology, ecology, practical life skills, design and technology. We all travel our own path in life, and listening to others share their journey and their experiences, and discovering the lessons that they learned along the way is fascinating and, more often than not, hugely inspiring.

Today, the Learning Annex is one of the gems of Sun Park. Hardly a day goes by without there being a talk or workshop. Many people travel to Sun Park solely to attend one of the hosted workshops.

One particularly interesting and memorable lecture I attended during my first visit to Sun Park was given by Simon Gosgrove, a retired social psychologist. His talk was about how and why we are influenced by the society in which we live. The talk was titled, 'Social Conformity: How We Can Be Manipulated By Society And What To Do About It'. As you might imagine, the auditorium was packed.

During the talk, Simon referred to several psychology experiments that he had been involved with during his career. One of the experiments demonstrated how most of us are heavily influenced by the people around us; our social network, friends, family and work colleagues. It was an experiment that has been repeated at Universities all over the world, each one coming to the same shocking conclusion.

"Imagine you're sitting in a room with seven other people", Simon said. "A supervisor enters the room, introduces herself, and explains that you're about to participate in a study about people's visual judgments and spatial awareness. She places two cards before you." Simon shows a slide of the two cards. The card on the left contains one vertical line. The card on the right displays three lines labelled A, B and C, each of varying length." Simon showed a slide of the two cards and continued. "Each person in the room is asked to choose which of the three lines on the right card is the same length as the line on the left card. Can you tell which one?"

Looking at the slide, it is seemed obvious to me, and should have been obvious to anyone with eyes to see, that C was the perfect match. The people in the audience laughed and murmured to themselves, probably thinking the same thing, but the chatter stopped when Simon continued.

"One by one the other six in the group choose B and then the supervisor turns to you. What would your answer would be?". More murmuring and chatter. At this point, I'm not as confident. If everyone else has said B, have I missed something? As I looked at the slide, C appeared to be the perfect match, but was it a trick of some kind? One of those optical illusions?

Simon smiles at the dilemma in the room. "The correct answer is, of course, C." he says. "But, would you believe that every time this experiment has been done, anywhere in the world, over seventy-five percent of people go with the rest of the group and give B as their answer rather than C which is the one that their own senses are telling them is correct! Why do they choose an answer that they know is wrong?"

Simon explained that when he and his colleagues interviewed the participants after the experiment, most of them said that they did not really believe the answers they gave were correct, but they had gone along with the group for fear of being ridiculed or being thought of as 'peculiar'.

"It's called 'Social Conformity'" said Simon. "Most people want to fit in with the people around them. We have a desire to be liked and accepted. That means that, all too often, we'll say and do things that conflict with what we know is right just to fit in.

"This phenomenon may be seen as a good or a bad thing, depending upon the values of the community in which we live. Whatever those values and beliefs are tend to become the values and beliefs that we adopt in our own lives."

Simon paused to let his words sink in. We don't like to think of ourselves as sheep. I certainly don't. But, as Simon's experiment had demonstrated, most of us are easily led. The evidence is incontrovertible.

"There is a lesson for us all here," Simon said, holding his finger up. "Choose your friends wisely.

This is why the most important gift parents can give their children is to make sure that they mix with other children who come from families with similar values. Once children get in with the 'wrong' crowd, all but the strongest characters are likely to end up accepting the values and beliefs of that crowd."

At the end of the talk, Simon invited questions from the audience. I asked, "what differentiates the twenty-five percent of people who are immune to social conformity from the seventy-five percent that choose to fit in?".

"That's a good question." Simon said. "We follow others more easily when we are unsure of ourselves, when we have no personal ethos, or when we seek approval from others to feel good about ourselves. A person who has a strong self-image and a strong set of values is much less likely to be swayed by a group."

Later that day I thought about the community and the ethos at Sun Park in relation to social conformity. I had seen people arrive by themselves at Sun Park with one set of values and, within days, they had adopted the community ethos. They would visibly change, their demeanour and attitude would change, and they would do things at Sun Park that they'd never think of doing back in the UK. It might be something as simple as feeling free to say 'hello' and engage in a conversation with a total stranger or, for some inexplicable reason, they might have the confidence or desire to try new activities that they could easily have done back in the UK, but didn't.

By their own admission, some people had, at first, been intolerant and short tempered, but after a matter of days, they found themselves becoming more accepting and patient. I'd never believed that people really change. I'd thought that character and personality were sort of fixed by our genes. But, I'd seen change happen at Sun Park with my own eyes. I'd experienced it myself. And, the change had come from the ethos.

I went to look for Greg to hear his thoughts. I suspected that the concept of Social Conformity had played a positive role here at Sun Park. Do people who come to Sun Park change through the desire to fit in? Or were other factors at play?

"Whilst it may be true that some people who come to Sun Park behave differently here than they might back in the UK just because they want to fit in with everyone else, most changes occur because here they're learning new things and having new experiences.

"People are influenced more through experiential conformity and informational conformity than social conformity," said Greg. "What does that mean? Informational conformity occurs when we base our decisions on new information. In other words, our values change when we become more informed and weigh up evidence that we might not have encountered before. Experiential conformity happens when we change our views or behaviour following a personal experience."

I asked Greg to give an example. "Of course," he said. "Let me see...you've been to The Green Kitchen?".

"Yes, of course." I said.

"So, you've met Shirley?".

"Yes."

"Okay, so most people in the West eat foods based upon social conformity. For example, they eat meat not because they need it or because it is healthy. They eat it because everybody in their social circle eats meat. Yet, nobody stops to think why they eat chicken and not owl, or pigs but not dogs, right? Why? Because it's the social norm here in the West to eat pigs. Yet, dogs are served on the menu in many restaurants in Asia. In Korea and China, dog meat is a delicacy, more succulent than pork. We don't eat dogs purely because it isn't the social norm. There is no logic or reason."

Greg had a point that was difficult to counter, so I didn't bother trying.

"That's social conformity." said Greg. "But here, people get exposed to new ideas. As you know, Shirley is a big advocate of a plant-based diet. She teaches how foods affect our health and she presents a compelling case, don't you think?".

I nodded. Shirley had certainly convinced me to try a meat-free diet.

"When you listen to her present the facts you tend to think more about what you eat, and some people decide to reduce the amount of meat they eat or stop eating meat altogether. This is informational conformity. Change brought about by becoming better informed, in this case, that a plant-based diet is better for our health.

"Then, in the Green Kitchen, Shirley demonstrates how to make plant-based meals. People come and taste meat-free, healthy options and some may change their diet because they enjoyed the veggie meals or because they felt healthier after trying a plant-based diet for a few weeks. That is what we'd call 'experiential conformity'. We change our behaviour as a result of our personal experiences."

The three conformities, as Greg had explained them, made sense to me.

"I think I understand." I said. "Social conformity happens subconsciously. We copy other people's behaviours to fit in. However, informational conformity relies more on reason and knowledge and experiential conformity comes through our feelings."

"You've got it," said Greg. "Social conformity is fine if the social norm is based upon sound principles, but it is still a thoughtless and emotionless response driven solely by the need for the approval of other people. And, the real problem is this; if the only reason someone behaves in a certain way is to fit in with the crowd, as soon as he or she leaves, their behaviour will very likely change to fit in with their new crowd. So, if someone eats a plant-based diet simply because that's what others around them are doing, then when they're around carnists, they'll eat meat.

"On the other hand, someone who adopts a plant-based diet due to information they have learned, for example, how a plant-based diet improves their health, or the cruelty involved in animal agriculture or how it damages the environment, the chances are they'll remain on a plant-based diet wherever they go.

"The same goes for people who adopt a plant-based diet through experiential conformity. We've seen a lot of that here; people who had arthritis or high blood pressure, even people who had diabetes, many experienced dramatic improvements in their health, within a matter of weeks. Once, you experience changes like that, you'd be a fool to go back to your old diet, right?"

I could see now why Sun Park affected the lives of so many people who visited. It wasn't that they were just trying to fit in as much as they were learning, growing and changing through the shared experience. I thought back to the end of Simon's lecture on Social Conformity. He had said that for a community to thrive, the individuals that made up the community needed to thrive. "Most of us need to develop a stronger sense of who we are," he said, "and instead of seeking the approval of others, make sure our behaviours align with our values.

"Once we have freed ourselves of the need to change just to please the people around us, we can start to change our lives by becoming better informed, trying different activities and seeing what works for us."

Part of the magic at Sun Park was that, through the shared experience, people changed. I was aware that I had changed during my time at Sun Park. I had no doubt that I had been influenced by some of the social norms; when the people around you are honest and trusting it kind of makes you want to do the same. When people smile and say 'hello', it feels natural to reciprocate and to engage in conversation.

I think it's also true to say that I changed as much from the things I learned. I felt different; healthier, certainly. You could put that down, at least in part, to the fresh air and sunshine. They would make better health a surety. No, there were other factors. Factors unrelated to the weather.

As I went to sleep that night, I realised that I hadn't taken a sleeping tablet since my first night at Sun Park. Even though the uncertainty about my future remained, I no longer felt anxious. I could hear Greg's mantra in my head, 'You're here today, and that's all that matters.' Just for today, I was fine. No, I was more than fine. Life was good. And, that was the last thought in my head as I shut my eyes and drifted into a deep sleep.

CHAPTER 18: SHOW ME YOUR GARDEN

*'Show me your garden and
I shall tell you what you are.'*
Alfred Austin

Sunrise at Sun Park is particularly peaceful. It's my favourite time of day. The only sound is the local bird song. I like to go for a walk, sometimes a light jog, along the beachfront to the end of the marina and back. One morning, whilst walking to the gate, I saw a man at the far end of the North quadrant, standing on a stepladder clipping the bushes.

Gary is a retired engineer from Colchester. He likes to get up early and start his day tending to the gardens. He trims hedges, cuts down branches, pulls out weeds. It looks like backbreaking work to me.

"Why do you do it?" I asked one morning.

"It's simple." he said, very matter-of-factly, "I enjoy gardening."

Gary was not the only person who liked to look after the gardens. Many visitors tended to the small garden in front of their apartment. They got pleasure planting, weeding and watering the gardens. In the same way that I would take a shopping bag out with me to pick up litter whenever I went for a walk in the local park back in the UK, some of the members and guests at Sun Park would see a section of garden that needed some help, and just do whatever needed doing.

One couple I met who were keen gardeners were David, a former head teacher and his wife, Liz, a retired nurse. David and Liz had their own allotment back in the UK. The first time I met them, they were planting some aloe cuttings into the flower beds at the top of the stairs in the South Quadrant. I was intrigued because although I had seen people watering plants in the little patch of garden belonging to their apartment, David and Liz were working on a section in the middle of the complex, far from any apartment and belonging to nobody.

David was pouring water from a washing up bowl onto the plants. I stopped to say good morning and find out what they were doing. I was particularly interested to find out why they were using a washing up bowl to manually water the gardens when there seemed to be a perfectly good automated, irrigation system which I had learned had been paid for and installed by the community.

David laughed. "When you put it like that, it probably does seem a bit daft. We're not the only ones though." David explained that there had been a severe drought the previous summer. All the Canary Islands had been affected. "If we had gone to a standard hotel," he said, "in all likelihood we would have been queueing up to complain at the reception with all of the other guests. But it's different here. Once we knew what was happening, we all got together and agreed to do whatever we could to conserve the limited water we had."

"That's amazing," I said. "What sort of things did you do?" I asked.

"Well, it doesn't seem like much. The usual things like not leaving the tap running when brushing teeth. Do you know that, for every minute you leave a tap running, you lose six litres of water? Times that by one hundred people cleaning their teeth for two minutes, twice a day and you've instantly saved over two thousand litres of water!"

I hadn't realised that so much water was wasted by something as innocuous as leaving a tap running when you brush your teeth and made a mental note to turn the tap off when I brushed my teeth in the future.

"We also recycled whatever water we used." said David. "We made sure to collect the water after washing and used it for the plants on the terraces."

"And we did the same for showers." added Liz.

"Really? You recycled your shower water?" I said.

"Yes." answered Liz. "It saved the gardens and most of us carried it on even after the water shortage ended. That's why you'll see people pouring buckets of water on the gardens from time to time."

I was aware that water is very precious, especially in the Canary Islands where it rains less than twenty days of the year. In some countries around the world, water is more expensive than petrol. In the past, when I stayed in hotels there were usually polite notices about conserving water. These were usually accompanied by requests for guests to reuse their towels rather than requesting new ones every day. If I'm honest, I'd never given those notices much thought. I'm not convinced many tourists do. But, here at Sun Park, wasting resources is anathema. Conservation is a big part of the ethos.

~

David and Liz were from Dundee in Scotland and this was their third visit to Sun Park. I asked them how they first heard about the resort.

"We were at Arrecife airport on our way home." said Liz. "We'd just spent a fortnight in a villa, outside Puerto del Carmen. We'd had a good holiday and really enjoyed our time on the island, but we were ready to go home. You know the feeling when you're happy to be going back to your friends and family?"

I nodded. Almost every two-week holiday I'd ever been on there had reached a point - usually after nine or ten days - when I was looking forward to going home. I'm not sure if it was boredom or whether I just I missed my home comforts. Perhaps both. Reflecting on it now, I think that there might be another factor; it may be that what we miss most is the people we leave behind. Whether staying in a hotel or in a villa, eventually there comes a time when we start to miss our friends and family.

Liz explained that she and David sat down next to a couple and they started chatting - as you do. The couple were raving about a place called 'Sun Park'. "They said that they had had such a good time that they had booked to go back and stay for six months the following year."

"Six months!" I said. "That's a long time to be away."

"That's what we thought, didn't we, David?" Liz said.

"We'd never heard anything like that before." David interjected. "The couple said it was 'holiday-living, a kind of 'home-from-home'. They spoke so highly about Sun Park that, when we got home, we decided to book an apartment for later in the year and come out and see what it was like for ourselves."

"And you obviously liked it," I said, "seeing as you have come back."

"We really love it here," smiled Liz.

"We really like the idea of being part of a community." said David. "I mean, much as I love Liz, I'm not sure either of us would want to spend six months by ourselves, alone in a villa."

Liz laughed. "That's true." she said. "Sun Park is a ready-made community. When people first arrive, if they don't know how it works, I can imagine it can be a bit bewildering. I mean there's no standard service and almost everything is run by the community. Even though Jean and Derek had told us about the place, it took us the best part of a week to appreciate why Sun Park is so unique."

"What makes the experience here unique for you?" I asked.

"There's a community spirit here that you just don't see anywhere else." Said David. "At least, I've never seen it."

The couple confirmed what so many others had said. To them, Sun Park was less about the place - the buildings, the facilities and the gardens - and more about the people who made up the community and the ethos they lived by.

Seeing everyone joining together and wanting to make a difference, made me want to join them and do my bit. In the past, I might have taken the view that, I've paid for my stay, so I'll use as much water as I want. Conserving water, or any resources for that matter, never entered my mind. From now on, I would be more mindful of how I consumed water and electricity. It felt good to contribute, even if only in a very small way.

CHAPTER 19: OLD FRIENDS, NEW FRIENDS

'Old friends pass away, new friends appear. It is just like the days. An old day passes, a new day arrives. The important thing is to make it meaningful: a meaningful friend - or a meaningful day.'
Dalai Lama

There's one thing that nobody who visits Sun Park is short of, and that's friends. From the moment, a person walks through the gates, they're made to feel welcome. The last place I can recall where I made so many friends, good friends, in such a short space of time, was at Summer Camp some forty-nine years ago. That may be because, in many ways, Sun Park is like a summer camp for adults. I've heard it referred to as 'holiday-living' for that very reason. But, there is another reason why everyone at Sun Park is so friendly; friendship is the cornerstone upon which the ethos has been built.

People may arrive on their own. At first, some may feel unsure, even anxious. However, change happens quickly; a smile, a conversation, a shared experience, an activity or an outing, and new, lifelong friendships are formed. You're no longer isolated and alone, you're part of an extended family. Friends, old and new, are a large part of what makes people return year after year to Sun Park.

~

Two great friends who met at Sun Park are Roy and Sid. I met them one morning whilst carrying some food shopping back from the local supermarket. Two men both wearing wide-brimmed cowboy hats were standing outside the front entrance of Sun Park. I couldn't help but smile. One of the men, Roy, was wearing camel boots, white socks pulled midway to his knees, khaki shorts and a baggy white tee shirt with 'Kiss Me Quick' printed in bold red on the front. The other, his cohort, Sid, was dressed in black trainers, short red socks, black adidas football shorts and a red football Manchester United football jersey. As I am a lifelong Manchester United fan, I immediately felt an instant kinship.

I approached and noticed that the men were wearing gardening gloves. Roy was holding a long-reach pick up aid - one of those mechanisms that enable you to pick things up without stretching or bending down - and, Sid was holding a black bin liner. I bid them good morning.

"Good morning young man", Roy replied in a broad Yorkshire accent.

"Morning." I replied.

"Are you staying at Sun Park?" Roy asked.

"Yes, I am," I said.

"Well, welcome, lad. I'm Roy an' this 'ere's my friend, Sid."

"Pleased to meet you both." I said offering my hand.

"What a beautiful day!" said Roy. "How lucky are we to be in this paradise?"

"Very!" I smiled back. "What are you both up to?".

"We thought these flower beds could do with a bit o' help." said Roy. I noticed that he had a plastic bag full of litter. "What's that?" I asked.

"Oh, now't really," he said. "Just pick'n up the odd bit of litter as we go."

I felt a certain kinship with Roy and Sid because, years ago when I had a dog, I would always take a shopping bag out with me and pick up bits of litter when I went on our walks through the local woods.

Meeting the two men reminded me of a story I had read years ago; John F Kennedy went to visit the NASA Space centre and came across a janitor who was holding a broom. "What are you doing?" the President asked. "Mr President," replied the Janitor, "I'm helping to send a man to the moon, sir!"

Roy and Sid had been coming back to Sun Park for the past three years and were well known in the community. Sun Park was much more than a holiday for these men, it had become their second home. Here, they were not just anonymous guests, they were part of a community. And, like so many others I had met, they wanted to be involved and contribute.

~

Later that day, I was talking with Eddie at the cafe in the main reception. I mentioned how impressed I had been after seeing Roy and Sid earlier in the day. "They are two wonderful human beings." said Eddie. "Do you know their background?".

I said that I had spoken to them for all of a few minutes. "Okay," said Eddie. "Have a you got a minute?".

"Of course." I said eager to find out more.

"Roy is a remarkable man." said Eddie. "He is in his mid-eighties, you know."

I'd placed him in his early seventies. Certainly, he looked younger than his years.

"You'd be hard-pushed to find another man that age who has Roy's strength or agility. Prior to coming to Sun Park, Roy looked after his younger sister. I believe her name was Alice. She suffered from pulmonary asbestosis, a chronic respiratory disease caused by exposure to asbestos. When she was in her twenties, Alice married an Australian chap and emigrated to New South Wales to start a new life with him. They'd been unable to have children but were happy enough until one day, years later, they received devastating news.

"A written notice from their local authority advised them that their house was unsafe. Apparently, the building contractor had used asbestos-based roofing insulation material, and tests showed that toxic particles were being released into the environment. Theirs wasn't the only house affected.

The same contractor had worked on a lot of the houses in the neighbourhood. It wasn't safe for anyone to stay in their homes and arrangements were made for their immediate evacuation. The houses were to be quarantined and destroyed, and eventually the residents received financial compensation equal to the estimated value of their homes which enabled them to relocate elsewhere.

"The problem for Alice and her husband was that they had done additional work in their attic space, turning it into a study. Without realising it, they had disturbed the toxic materials and subsequent health tests confirmed that both Alice and her husband Martin had been infected."

I knew about asbestosis. There is no cure, no treatment. The micro particles become lodged in the lung tissue and, from then on, there is no stopping the gradual degeneration of tissue.

"Alice's husband was the first to succumb." continued Eddie. "Almost ten years to the day of the original notice, he passed away. His condition had been the worse of the two because he did the renovation work himself, or because he used the attic every week day as his study.

"Alice had just turned sixty-eight and although her brother, Roy, was ten years her senior, he became her carer. At the age of seventy-eight and suffering with arthritic knees and high blood pressure, Roy travelled half-way around the world to bring his sister home. He looked after her, day and night, until the disease finally took her last breath, five years later.

"I believe that it was at his sister's wake that a close friend mentioned Sun Park to Roy. He had no desire to go anywhere or do anything, but his friend left a brochure with him and insisted that Roy should go and visit. A few months later, he did, and the rest, as they say, is history. He came, and he never went back."

"That is quite a story." I said. "What about his friend, Sid?".

"The two met here and instantly hit it off. Sid is quite a character too. He's registered blind, you know."

I had no idea.

"He has a condition called macular degeneration. Don't start feeling sorry for him though." said Eddie. "We don't do that here. People don't want sympathy. They just need a little support and help from time to time. Sid might not be able to see as well as you or I, but he can find his way around Sun Park better than anyone. When he first came to Sun Park, Roy put brightly coloured stickers around the resort to help Sid. Bright yellow for paths and corridors and bold red for stairs. With the stickers in place, Sid didn't need Roy or anyone else to find his own way around the complex.

"That was a few years ago and I don't think Sid needs the stickers anymore. He knows exactly where everything is. I'll tell you something funny... a while back we had a power cut one evening and, believe it or not, it was Sid who acted as guide helping those people who didn't have their mobile phones with them get to their apartments."

"Seriously?"

"Absolutely. Crazy, isn't it? A genuine case of the blind leading the sighted. He was awesome!"

~

Over the years there have been countless times that I've witnessed people arriving at Sun Park alone and friendless, and within a matter of days those people have experienced personal transformation. None was more touching than Jonathan, a sixty-seven-year-old widower from a small town in Derbyshire. I met Jonathan one evening on my way to the Marigold bar. He was a short, rotund bald man, sitting alone, and smoking a cigarette. I said hello and introduced myself.

"I'm just getting myself a beer." I said. "Can I get you one?".

"I never say no to a beer." he said looking up. "Thank you."

I went into the bar. It was still early in the evening but already there were groups of people sitting around tables. George and his wife Evelyn were among them.

"Evening, Stan! How are you, mate?"

"Great, thanks." I replied. "How are you, George?"

I walked over to say 'hello'. I recognised a few faces, but George introduced me to the crowd. "Would you like to join us?", George said.

"I'd love to, but I'm just getting a beer for a chap I met outside." I replied. "Maybe later?".

I took two bottles of San Miguel from the fridge, put a few euros in the honesty box and then went back outside.

I handed a bottle to Jonathan and we clinked our bottles. "Cheers." I said. "Cheers."

We sat chatting outside the bar. In winter months, although the days can be beautifully warm, when the sun sets, it can leave a slight chill in the air. I couldn't complain though. If I'd been in the UK, I'd have needed a quilted ski coat and thermals to sit outside in the evening at this time of year.

I don't know how long Jonathan and I sat chatting together. I do know that we went through a few more bottles of beers though. We talked about the usual things; the government, the European Union, the proposed changes to the football rules. Jonathan was a longsuffering Derby fan. In recent history, the team had always managed to end up in the top ten of the Championship. A few seasons they had reached third place, but promotion to the coveted Premiership had eluded them. Sport - and particularly, football - has this amazing ability to enable strangers to connect. It may seem superficial, but you never know where a connection can lead.

There was a momentary silence before Jonathan said, "You know what Stan, this is the first time I've sat down and had a drink with someone in over eight years."

I didn't know how to answer that. Fortunately, I didn't need to as he continued. "To tell the truth, it's the first time I've been on holiday in eight years too." he said.

I didn't respond in words. I could sense that Jonathan wanted to offload something, and I let him continue at his own pace. He took a breath and continued.

"My son died." he said.

"I'm so sorry. What happened?". Jonathan's eyes were glistening. "He was... murdered." he said.

I put my hand on his arm, and said nothing. And we sat there in silence. Moments later he stood up and said "Thanks, Stan.".

It was still early by my clock. 9:30pm, but I could see he wanted to be alone. That's part of the wonder of Sun Park. Sometimes we all need to be alone and, when we do, we can close the door, or walk along the coast. It's comforting to know that, at other times, when you need company, there's always someone with whom you can share a drink.

"Goodnight," I said. He put his hand on my shoulder. And said "thanks". I hadn't done anything other than listen, but perhaps, at that moment, it was all he needed.

~

The next time I saw Jonathan was two days later at the Expressive Writing Workshop. After hearing several glowing recommendations about the workshop, I had decided to sign up. The workshop was run by a therapist from Shropshire, a man by the name of Joseph Barrow. Joseph explained the science behind 'Expressive Writing' (which is also referred to as Writing Therapy). "It is very simple," he said. "It involves just 15-20 minutes of writing about subjects that still bother you or which still raise strong emotions."

Joseph explained that by releasing our thoughts and feelings onto paper, we unburden our subconscious and this leads to a wide range of physiological and emotional changes. "As an example,", Joseph said, "studies have shown that our liver function improves, our immune system receives a boost, we see an increase in white blood cells, a reduction in stress hormones... the overall effects are remarkable."

Even more powerful than the physical effects were the mental and emotional benefits. Joseph explained that Expressive Writing can be as effective as counselling, group therapy and even anti-depressants in helping people cope during times of intense stress, trauma, loss and grief in addition to boosting our self-esteem.

He showed us research papers showing that the writing exercise released negative emotions including anger, resentment, and jealousy, and the process stopped what Joseph called 'mental rumination' which he explained was when we constantly mull over things in our minds. Studies had shown that Expressive Writing alleviated anxiety, improved sleep and subjects' working memories typically improved by a factor of seven!

"Controlled clinical trials have demonstrated that Expressive Writing was as effective – and, in some cases, more effective - than many commonly prescribed medical drugs in alleviating the symptoms of rheumatoid arthritis and asthma." said Joseph. "It has even been shown to help people overcome alcohol and drug addiction, arthritis, cancer, eating disorders, HIV infection, cystic fibrosis, chronic pain, insomnia, post-traumatic stress disorder, and depression. And, as crazy as it sounds, postoperative healing was found to be significantly faster when patients did these same Expressive Writing exercises."

By the time Joseph had finished explaining what Expressive Writing was, how it worked, and the associated benefits, we were all eager to try it for ourselves. It involved a twenty-minute writing session performed on four consecutive days. In each session, we were told to sit and write about anything that still troubled us. It could be about a person, or an event; it could be about something that happened in the past, something that might happen in the future, or something that is current and still ongoing in our lives. We could write about the same thing each day, or entirely different things. The only requirement was we had to write during the allotted time in each session about something that raised strong feelings.

I wrote about my childhood on one day, the sudden loss of my mother on the next, the death of my wife on the third and, on the fourth and final day, I wrote about being made redundant and my worries about the future. During each session some people wept openly, some finished their sessions feeling exhausted. Narrating and reliving past traumas consumes a lot of energy.

I was very glad to have done the workshop with the group rather than alone. Everyone was supportive of each other. We had written alone, and recorded our deepest and, perhaps darkest experiences, but it was a journey we had made together. After east session, there were hugs all round and by the time the course had finished, everyone who had participated felt a special connection. The experience was everything and more that we had been led to expect.

Joseph explained that there was no need to discuss anything with others afterwards. What we had written was, after all, deeply personal. However, it was evident that many people were profoundly affected by the experience, and the changes in their demeanour were very noticeable. I can only speak for myself but, by the end of the fourth session, I felt as if I had set down a heavy load that I had been carrying around with me for years.

I felt lighter, calmer, and free of anxiety. I was sleeping soundly, with no medications, and to my delight, my skin was virtually completely clear. My elbows and knees were smooth. No more dry, scaly patches anywhere. I know, of course, that a lot of other things would have contributed to these improvements; the meditation, the weather, and some of the other activities like Tai Chi and swimming. I was eating fresher, healthier food too. However, some of the others who had been in the Expressive Writing workshop reported similar health benefits, and there was no doubt in my mind that the exercises had created some sort of shift inside me.

I saw Jonathan early one evening towards the end of the week. He was sitting outside the Marigold in the same place where I had first met him. Only this time, he wasn't alone. He was among a small crowd, all playing cards. I stopped to say, 'good evening'. They seemed a friendly bunch but, then again, as I'd come to learn, friendliness is something of the norm at Sun Park. I left them to their game and headed into the Marigold to get a drink and see who was there.

"Hey Stan!". I turned around. It was Jonathan, "Catch you later!"

CHAPTER 20: A TIME TO LIVE

'Learn to enjoy every minute of your life. Be happy now. Don't wait for something outside of yourself to make you happy in the future. Think how really precious is the time you have to spend, whether it's at work or with your family. Every minute should be enjoyed and savoured. '
Earl Nightingale

Everyone loves Melanie. She's outgoing, friendly and full of vitality. All attractive qualities, but the reason she is so loved is that she can empathise with anyone, she is one of Life's carers. If you've got a problem, or need help or advice, you can ask any of the members at Sun Park and they'll all be happy to help, if they can. However, Melanie seems to be constantly helping people. The first time I saw her, she was on the terrace, going in and out of the main reception, helping a couple who had left their medications back in the UK. Melanie took them to the on-site clinic where they got a prescription and then to the local pharmacy. It was a simple matter, but made that much easier thanks to Melanie's intervention.

I wasn't surprised to learn that, back in the UK, Melanie had been a professional 'Stage Two' carer, looking after terminally ill cancer patients. Stage Two is the official term used by the medical profession when death is imminent. Every terminal illness ends with two distinct stages; the first stage, also known as the pre-active stage, usually starts a few weeks before we die. In this stage, patients are typically confused and lethargic. They tend to become restless and have difficulty sleeping. Often, a patient becomes emotionally withdrawn and unresponsive.

When someone enters the second stage of dying, the exact moment when their body stops functioning can't be predicted with accuracy. "The person leaves when they are ready", Melanie says. "You know it when it happens." This is why carers are there with them until the end, holding their hand and comforting them as best they can. The stage two carer is there to 'keep a vigil'. The patient may not be able to respond in words or gestures, but stage two carers will tell you that consciousness can remain until the last breath.

Melanie loves her job. "It is a huge privilege" she says, "to be able to comfort someone as their spirit leaves their body." She has witnessed dozens of people's final moments, and she is convinced that death is not an end, but rather another beginning. "Being a stage two carer is, for me, a lot like being a midwife." she said. "I don't see it as a job to help people end their lives as much as helping people move on to another stage in their journey."

How could you not be moved by that sentiment? When my time comes, I hope that I'll be fortunate enough to have someone like Melanie by my bedside.

When you hear Melanie's story and see her in action, helping anyone in need, it is easy to appreciate why she is so loved throughout Sun Park. She has her flaws, of course, as we all do. Why she continues to hasten her own demise by smoking cigarettes is something I'll never understand. She can't explain her addiction and she has no desire to quit. But, to be fair, for whatever reason, one in five female nurses in the UK - and over 540,000 nurses in the USA, are heavy smokers, even though they know better than most, that it is self-destructive. But, who am I to judge? All I know is that Melanie has a beautiful spirit. Ask virtually anybody at Sun Park and they'll tell you the same thing.

I have seen Melanie help so many people, in many ways. In one instance, she helped a couple who wanted to extend their stay. The process of extending your stay at Sun Park was quite straightforward, it is just a matter of going online or making a phone call. This is explained on the website and it's also mentioned in the welcome booklet. However, Melanie had overheard the couple on the main terrace telling a new guest that they weren't very sure the best way to go about it, so she offered to help. She took them into the main reception, sat down at one of the computers, and clicked a live chat button which connected with a live operator. Within a matter of minutes, the couple had a confirmed two-week extension to their stay.

Whilst I was at Sun Park an incident happened that typified Melanie's generosity of spirit. She had noticed earlier on in the day that her neighbour was looking very pale so, in the evening, she knocked on her neighbour's door to make sure she was okay. When her neighbour finally answered the door, Melanie could immediately tell that her neighbour wasn't well. Her face was ashen and she was running a high fever. Melanie took her to the medical clinic just along the road. The doctor examined the woman and then said she had sun stroke. The remedy was rest, a cold, damp towel to the forehead, paracetamol and plenty of liquids.

Melanie walked her neighbour back to her apartment, gave her two paracetamols and a large bottle of water. When the woman woke up the following morning, she found a note beside her bed. *'If you need anything, just knock on my door. Love, Melanie xx'*

That lady never forgot Melanie's kindness. "It was my second day and I'd had a bit too much sun and not enough fluids. It could have easily been a disaster and ruined the whole week, but thanks to Melanie, I was fine the following day. Honestly, I was so touched that someone who was a complete stranger to me, went out of her way to look after me that night." she said.

As soon as the lady had recovered, Melanie introduced her to friends. She got involved in some of the activities and, like so many others, she ended up enjoying herself so much that she decided to extend her stay.

"I made some wonderful friends." she said. "One night, a group of us ended up in Melanie's apartment eating tapas, drinking and chatting into the early hours. "Do you know," she said with genuine animation, "it was like I had travelled back in time. It reminded me of when I was a teenager at summer camp. My friends and I would close the curtains and stay up. We'd have a midnight snack, play games, or just talk, sometimes until sunrise. How often do you get the chance to relive the happiest times of your past?".

Hearing the woman's story made me think about my own summers as a teenager. Like her, I had been fortunate enough to have gone to summer camps in my early teens. I remember staying at what was a boarding school in Oxfordshire, surrounded by rolling fields, woods and a lake. I hadn't known a soul when I stepped on to the bus, but by the time we arrived, I'd made a new best friend and the two of us had dates with two blonde sisters who were sitting behind us. That turned out to be a very special summer.

Chapter 21: The Game Of Life

'We cannot change the cards we are dealt,
just how we play the game.'
Randy Pausch

Most weekday afternoons at Sun Park, at around 4:30pm, you'll find twenty or more people sitting at tables in groups of four playing a card game first popularised by the nineteenth century Russian community living in Istanbul. Bridge - the English pronunciation of *Biritch* - is played by over two hundred million people around the world. Card games are fun, but Bridge seems to grip people like no other. 'I wouldn't mind being in jail' Warren Buffet, one of the game's many high-profile fans, once famously said, 'if I had three cellmates who were decent players and who were willing to keep the game going 24 hours a day.'

The Bridge club at Sun Park is organised by Tim Silverman who, despite having lived in Sydney, Australia for most of his adult life, speaks with a distinctly North London, English accent. I met Tim one afternoon as I was arriving back from a walk along the beachfront. It was 4:20pm when I passed through the main reception. Tim was laying packs of cards out on the tables with notepads and pencils.

"Hi." I said. "What's going on?"

Tim looked up. "Hi there." he said. "We're just getting ready for Bridge club. Do you play?"

I told him that it had been over five years since I had last played. My wife and I used to play sporadically with friends, but I wasn't a particularly accomplished player. Neither myself nor my wife invested the time it takes to learn the finer points of the game.

'That's not a problem." Tim said. "We've got all levels here from complete beginners up to Bridge Masters. You're welcome to join us if you like."

I had nothing planned and it was a chance to get to know more people, so I accepted Tim's invitation. A group of people walked into the room and more were arriving from the terrace. Tim led me to the far table and introduced me to the two ladies and one man who were seated there.

"Linda, Sylvia, Tony meet Stan." he said. "Stan hasn't played for a while so I thought it might be a good idea for him to partner you Linda."

"Of course." Linda said.

'Thanks. I haven't played in a very, very long time," I said, keeping expectations low.

"Oh, don't worry." said Linda. "I only started playing a few months ago".

Linda was a petite lady with bright green eyes and rich, auburn-coloured hair, wavy and free-flowing to her shoulders. During the tea break she told me her story. She had divorced from her husband nine years ago. They had been together for eighteen years which, she said, had not always been easy. Her ex-husband was a compulsive gambler. The final straw came when she discovered that he had gambled and lost their family home. "We lost everything." she said. "Or, rather *he* lost everything."

I shook my head, not knowing what to say.

"Anyway," Linda said smiling, "That's all in the past. I'm here now..."

"And that's all that matters!" we all said completing Greg's mantra.

I asked Linda why, as a single woman, she had chosen Sun Park over, say, a singles holiday. "To be totally honest, I'm not interested in getting married again and I think most people who go on those singles holidays are looking for a partner. I'm not. I like my independence. I just don't want to be alone.

"Back in the UK, so many of my friends are couples and, although I am always included in whatever they're doing, being single in a room full of couples isn't a lot of fun."

I understood exactly what she meant. In the years since my wife had died, I had been the odd one out at a number of dinner parties and supper quizzes. In the end, I declined invitations. As a single person, sometimes you can feel more alone in a crowd, than sitting by yourself at home.

"At Sun Park, I'm not the odd one out." Linda said. "I mean, there are plenty of single people here as well as couples, and it's also so easy to meet people who share your interests. That's important to me."

Unlike Linda, Sylvia and Tony were both married, although not to each other. Sylvia had fair skin, light blue eyes and blonde hair tied back in a ponytail. Tony was a tall heavily built man with silver-grey hair. He wore light metal rimmed glasses. Even though they were both happily married, Sylvia and Tony came to Sun Park for the same reason as Linda. They came for the experience, for the ethos. They loved their partners, but they didn't want to be with them twenty-four hours a day, seven days a week. This was partly because they and their partners didn't share all of the same interests. Bridge was just one example; neither Sylvia nor Tony's partners liked card games.

"Here we can do activities together or apart." Sylvia said. "I think it is good that my husband and I don't do everything together. I love him to bits, but if we were together for twenty-four hours a day, I'd end up throttling him."

Tony laughed. "Same here. My wife will tell you that she dreaded the day when we would leave full-time work. We all need a little space to do our own thing. You know? It's not healthy to be in one another's pockets the whole time. At Sun Park, she can do what she likes, I do what I like. Some things we do together. It's perfect."

It was interesting to me how one place could appeal to singles and couples, but for completely opposite reasons. Single people, like Linda and myself, come because they don't want to always be alone, whereas couples come because they don't want always be together. I guess it is about finding the right balance between being free to pursue your own interests, and being able to enjoy shared experiences.

After the tea break, we swapped tables, which meant that, in the second session, we ended up playing with different people. By the end, I'd realised that I'd forgotten how much I used to enjoy playing Bridge. I walked over to Tim who was putting the cards away to thank him.

"So, you enjoyed it?" he said.

"Very much." I said.

"That's great. We play most days so come along whenever you like."

"Thanks, I will." I replied.

I asked Tim how long he had been playing for.

"Over thirty years", he said. "I was hooked from the first time I played. I just fell in love with it."

"What was it you loved about the game?" I asked.

"Firstly, it's a mental workout." he said. "It's more mentally and intellectually challenging than any other card game. I mean, anyone who likes a challenge, enjoys playing Bridge.

"Secondly, it's a stress reliever. You have to concentrate and be completely focussed throughout each hand. There's no room for any other thoughts and so any worries seem to fade into the background when you start playing.

"Thirdly, Bridge helps you develop a strong memory and improves logical thinking. You need good communication skills too. Many psychologists say that if you to develop a strong memory and keep your mind active, one of the best things you can do is play Bridge."

There's no question that Tim was correct in everything he said. Playing Bridge does require concentration and you do need to be able to apply logical thinking and memorise the cards as you play. If you're looking for an easy card game that doesn't require much thought, Bridge wouldn't be the game for you. But, if you're looking for a game that is always challenging, where there's always something new to learn, there's nothing better.

"Scientists at the University of California demonstrated that Bridge boosts our immune system too." said Tim, putting the packs of cards, score pads and pencils into a box. "They say it is something to do with how it stimulates specific parts of the brain.

"All those things aside" he said, "Bridge is a wonderful metaphor for Life!"

Now I was confused. A metaphor for Life? In what way?

"In many ways." said Tim. "Firstly, like the game of life, bridge is not a game you play alone. You need other people. And, to play Bridge well, you need to communicate and cooperate. I think those are essential life skills.

"One of the most important life lessons when playing Bridge is how much more important it is to have the right attitude than it is to have the right circumstances."

"Err, I'm not sure I understand what you mean." I said.

Tim smiled. "When you learn to play Bridge, you quickly discover that the cards you're dealt are not as important as how you play the game. You can be dealt the best hand in the world, but if you don't focus and plan, and if you don't communicate well with your partner, you'll get nowhere. Similarly, you can be dealt a stinker of a hand, but still come out victorious."

"Ah, I think I understand." I said.

"In Life," Tim continued, "any one of us can be dealt a shitty hand; some people are born with severe physical disadvantages, some suffer with life-threatening diseases, and others are left injured and disadvantaged by an accident that happened through no fault of their own. But, if you surround yourself with friends and play the game of Life to the best of your ability - thoughtfully, rationally, and with optimism - you can still enjoy a full and happy life."

Tim was right, of course. In my short time at Sun Park, I'd met some amazing people who had suffered severe setbacks in their lives. Gordon had been born a Thalidomide victim, Dennis had been struck by Polio as an infant, and Sid had lost his eyesight to macular degeneration. Don, Paula and Phil were coping with Multiple Sclerosis. I don't think that many people go through life without being touched by tragedy or loss. It's true that some loss and some tragedies are worse than others but, in the end, what matters is how we respond. No doubt, this was why those people at Sun Park who had suffered great tragedy and loss, appeared to be so happy. Perhaps Tim's analogy wasn't far off the mark? The people at Sun Park played a better game because they didn't play alone. They played together, part of a team, surrounded by friends. They played with people they loved and respected, people who they knew would always be there for them.

CHAPTER 22: STAND BY ME

'Walking with a friend in the dark is better than walking alone in the light.'
Helen Keller

Every Friday morning, as Sun Park opens its doors to the public, a group of musicians and singers within the community put on a performance in the main lobby. The music on Social Fridays started out with one saxophonist, Sam Bakewell, a musician from Essex who, after a hectic run of gigs prior to and during the festive season, liked to take the first two months of each calendar year relaxing at Sun Park. Sam was then joined by Chris, a guitar player from Durham, and weeks later Vanessa, who sings in her local Church choir back in Didsbury, asked if she could join them. The three inspired other community members to get involved. Chris ran informal classes teaching both the guitar and banjo, and a community choir was formed.

Social Fridays became renowned throughout Playa Blanca as the 'concert morning'. Locals and holidaymakers are treated to a few hours of assorted live music including folk, country and western, gospel, jazz, and even some rhythm and blues. Among the choir is Henrietta, a short, stout lady in her seventies, but with energy that women thirty years her junior would envy.

Henrietta confided that she hadn't always been as energetic or happy. In fact, she had been plagued with depression for most of her adult life. She had worked as a bookkeeper, and had ended up working from home, looking after the accounts of three clients.

"Things got worse when I turned sixty," she said. "I had been in and out of hospital many times during my life, but I think the constant feeling of isolation began to overwhelm me. My doctor said I was depressed. I don't think we're made to live alone, by ourselves. Do you know, Stan, that there are over two million people in the UK over the age of seventy-five who don't see or speak to a soul for thirty days at a time? Loneliness is a killer."

I nodded. "What changed for you?".

"I found Sun Park," she said. "I was reading a magazine in the waiting room at my doctor's surgery and I came across this 'inspiring community of active, independent over fifties.' So, I thought that I'd try it out. And, it turned out to be the best decision I've ever made."

I smiled. It was a response I was hearing from almost everybody I came across.

"I'll admit, it was a bit strange at first," she continued, "but then I met Gloria, who has become my best friend. A few days later, I was sitting on my terrace with her and few other people, and I just thought, 'Hen, you're happy!'. For the first time, in years, I felt...carefree.

"When I came here, I was unsure what to expect but, within a few days, I felt a change. I felt safe here. I didn't feel alone. I mean I don't know anywhere else where can you can knock on a stranger's door and be welcomed as a friend. Do you?"

I knew exactly what Henrietta was alluding to. Even though I had been at Sun Park for less than a fortnight, I already felt part of the community. I had been welcomed by everyone I had met and, for the first time in years, I was part of something. I felt renewed, as if my life had just been kickstarted. There were so many choices, so many things to do.

"So, I take it you're no longer depressed?" I asked.

"Absolutely not!" said Henrietta. "I saw a local doctor here, and she agreed that if I felt that much better, I could come off my antidepressants, and I never looked back. I don't take any tablets at all now, and I've never felt better."

"That's fantastic!" I said. Henrietta smiled, her bright green eyes shining with enthusiasm. "I don't think you'd call Sun Park a medicine," she said, "but it is very therapeutic."

A woman called from the far side of the room, "Hen! We're up!".

"Looks like I'm needed. Great meeting you, Stan." Henrietta said. She kissed me on each cheek, stood up and walked over to the woman who was beckoning her over.

I sat at the table and watched Henrietta join the choir. They sang without musical accompaniment, a cappella, 'Stand by Me' by Ben E King.

When the night has come, and the way is dark,
And that moon is the only light you see.
No I won't be afraid, no I-I-I won't be afraid
Just as long as the people come and stand by me.

The reception was packed, and I have no doubt that the song was just background music to many of those there that day. It wasn't a concert, after all. The song may have been lost to some, muffled by the sound of people chatting and laughing. But, I was transfixed by the singers and the powerful lyrics of the song. If I'm honest, it stirred emotions. Sometimes, all we need to find our way through the dark and difficult times in our lives are friends, people who will stand by our side.

CHAPTER 23: HOW TO START A COMMUNITY

'Coming together is a beginning; keeping together is progress; working together is success.'
Henry Ford

How does an ethos such as the one I had discovered at Sun Park evolve? Is it something that just happens by chance, or is it the result of careful planning? More importantly, how can the ethos be replicated elsewhere? These were questions that I thought about often. One thing I was quite sure of, something like this doesn't happen by accident.

I asked Greg and Christina, both of whom said that they could take no credit for the ethos. They did acknowledge that this was what they had intended, but all they had done was lay the foundations for the ethos to flourish.

I asked many people staying at Sun Park for their thoughts about the origins of the ethos, but didn't find anybody who knew exactly how and why the ethos had evolved at Sun Park. Then, one afternoon I met a man who had some answers.

Richard Dunston is a professor of sociology. He still works at the Milton Keynes campus of the University of Bedfordshire. He and his wife, June, have been coming to Sun Park from its inception. Richard has a stature befitting his status in life. He is a tall, slim man. He has pale, freckled skin and a receding hairline which has largely retained its ginger colouring, although it is was peppered with grey around the sides. June is a good head shorter and has long auburn hair tied back into a ponytail. Unlike Richard, she tanned easily. Despite coming from the north of England, June had the type of skin colouring usually associated with people of dark, Mediterranean lineage.

I met Richard and June on the main terrace one morning. I was interested to learn about their experiences at Sun Park. In particular, how did they first find out about it? And what did they love about it?

"Why do I love it here?" Richard said. "That's easy. The ethos here reminds a lot of my home town."

"That's interesting," I said. "Where are you from?"

"A tiny town on the outskirts of Milton Keynes called Wolverton."

Wolverton, I learned, is not the kind of place that you'd expect a resident to boast about. It's a far cry from the sprawling, neatly designed modern developments upon which Milton Keynes was built. But, Wolverton has something in abundance that has been overlooked by many developers of new towns in the UK for decades... a sense of community.

"To be frank, it is not a pretty place," said Richard. It consists of long, narrow straight streets, rows upon rows of terraced houses. Nothing fancy. No thatched roofs or country mansions or vast estates. Viewed from above, you'd just see streets and paths that criss-cross forming a geometric pattern. But what the buildings lack in character, is more than compensated for by the community."

"Really?" I asked. "Why have you got such a great community?"

"It's interesting. I think there may be several reasons," said Richard. "Firstly, in Wolverton, just about everything you need is within walking distance; the schools - infant, junior and senior schools - are all within a short walk. The doctor's surgery, the hospital, the shopping mall are all within easy access too.

"We've got churches, a mosque, pubs, working men's clubs, arts facilities, sports facilities...no matter where you live in Wolverton, they're all within walking distance. We've got a bus terminus, a railway station, a cinema. Everything is within easy reach.

"I think a lot comes from the network of back alleys and narrow streets because it allows children to play safely outside their homes and, more importantly, it means that neighbours are always meeting and connecting with one another as they go about their day.

The ability to connect with your neighbours is absolutely crucial to the creation of community. The houses are close because the streets were built in the days before cars dominated, so when you come out of your house you can't help but bump into people. As you take your children to school, whether through the back alleys or along the streets, you are forced to engage and connect with everyone else."

I thought about what Richard was saying and it made sense. Here at Sun Park, spacious though the resort is, the apartments are very much like terraced houses, separated only by a single wall. Sure, you had privacy, but sit at the front of your terrace or balcony, or walk along any path to the swimming pools, or gardens or main terrace and reception, and you were guaranteed to cross paths with others. There was never a feeling of isolation that you so often find in the big cities.

"The other thing Wolverton offers," continued Richard, "is the opportunity to join in a wide range of activities and community events. All completely free. There's no paid subscription or exclusive club. There are no strings attached. Everybody is welcome to get involved either as a participant or a spectator. And, if you don't want to be involved, that's fine too.

"I remember before the 2012 Olympics and the Paralympics when thousands of people came into their towns to watch the Olympic flame be carried through. I was there on the streets of Winslow, having waited all morning, and it was fantastic. It lasted no more than twenty seconds, but we weren't just there to see the flame. I mean, we could have got a better view watching on TV. We wanted to be part of something, and isn't that what a community is all about?

"When I first arrived here at Sun Park, it reminded me a lot of Wolverton. People engage with you. There is this wonderful sense of community. Here you're part of something. Helping develop this place and work on projects with other people who were staying here was, in some strange way, kind of appealing. You know...we were part of this wonderful community.

"I think that it was because Sun Park was like an open canvas – and, in many respects, still is – that the ethos evolved the way it has."

"Why do you say that?" I asked.

"Well, the fact that so much needed to be done meant that there were lots of opportunities to contribute. There were all kinds of projects that people could be involved with."

"But weren't you coming on holiday to enjoy yourself rather than to organise activities and events for everyone?"

Richard smiled. "You're right, we did come away to enjoy ourselves. Originally, we had come away to relax and do all the usual things you'd expect to do when you're on holiday. Walking, swimming, tennis, read a book by the pool. Don't get me wrong, we did all those things. That's all great for a short two-week holiday, but when you're away for a much longer period, you want something more. We enjoyed getting involved with activities and events, and helping on various projects."

"The Marigold was my favourite." Esther said. "That was a fun few days."

"Of course," said Richard. "The Marigold. A lot of people helped clear it out, then paint it. We built the bar and, right at the end when all of those things were done, we refurbished the Bar-B-Q outside."

I still found it amazing that people would come away for what was, to all intents and purposes, a holiday and spend part of that time working to transform the resort in which they were staying.

"But, Stan," he said, "it didn't feel like work. It was really a lot of fun. Being involved in the projects, even if only for a few hours each day, brought everyone closer together. We all had a common mission."

"It was like being at a summer camp." said June. "We thoroughly enjoyed our time and when the time came to leave we felt like we'd really made a difference. Everyone did. And, that's a great feeling."

"There's no doubt that we formed much closer friendships working together on some of the projects here." added Richard, "Look around..." he said pointing to the pools and gardens in bloom. There was no question that the gardens were beautiful, resplendent in colour and aroma. "It feels good to know that we played a small part in this... we're really proud of what's been achieved so far."

I could see that contributing in the ways Richard and June had mentioned must bring a great sense of satisfaction.

"In most resorts, you arrive, and everything is provided for you." Richard said. "But, I like the fact that here at Sun Park you can be a participant rather than just a spectator. If you want to be served all the time and have everything done for you, then this really isn't the place for you." said Richard. "But, when you come to a place like Sun Park, just as if you were to make your home in Wolverton, you have an opportunity to be a part of a community. You don't just experience change, you create change."

I nodded. I had a lot of fun on my second day, joining over twenty people to help set up the Ching-Ching Chiringuito bar in the South Gardens. With so many people helping, it took less than a few hours; we washed everything down, cleaned and wiped the cupboards and surfaces and scrubbed all the tables and chairs. By the end, we had turned a rundown shack into a really cool outside bar. Sitting there later that evening drinking a beer with some of the guys was hugely satisfying.

"The thing is this," said Richard, "when I first came here and became part of this amazing community, I thought my days of having any meaningful contribution to society were long gone. We came here for a holiday experience and we left having a life experience."

"What do you mean?" I asked.

"Well, if you ask most people what they want out of life, you'll get all sorts of answers. Most focus on their happiness without really thinking what it means to be happy. Often, it's bigger and better - cars, houses, holidays...and there's nothing wrong in that. But, I can assure you - because it has been demonstrated repeatedly, that what we really want is a meaningful life.

"We want to feel like we have a purpose, we want to connect and engage, we want to be part of something bigger than ourselves. And, when our time comes, we would all like to leave having contributed something. You know, to have lived and left a mark, leaving the world a little bit better for having lived. And, you learn that here.

"You come, you meet friends, you participate, and by the time you come to leave, you look around and you can see that you were part of something. When the time comes for you to check out, you will probably leave having made a crowd of new friends, but you may also take away a sense of satisfaction, knowing that you've made a difference whilst you were here. Your life will have been enriched by the experience, but this magical place - this wonderful community – will also be a little bit better off for you having been here."

CHAPTER 24: WE ARE ALL CONNECTED

*'What is it in human beings that helps us keep a
healthy sense of ourselves - helps us keep a sense of
meaning in our lives - in the face of stressors? The
number one thing that human beings need is actually
connectedness - connection with other human
beings.'*
Dr David Servan-Schrieber

As the sun was setting one evening, I sat on the main
terrace talking to Greg about Life. "According to
Socrates" Greg said, "the highest pursuit in life is
happiness. The one thing we all want above all else
is simply to be happy."

I confessed to Greg that, for most of my adult life,
happiness has alluded me. I don't know why.

"Let me ask you a question" Greg said. "If you were
going to invest right now in your future - and I'm not
just talking about investing your money, but
investing your time and your energy - with the aim
of assuring your future well-being and happiness,
what would you do?"

"Hmm. That's a tough one." I said. Not having an
answer, threw the ball back into his court. "What
would you do?"

Greg smiles. "I'd make sure I kept in touch with
friends and family."

Ah. Nice answer, I thought to myself. Why hadn't I thought of it?

"A number of years back, I watched a lecture by Steve Wozniak, the co-founder of Apple," he said. "Wozniak was the technical brains behind the company and looks at the world and the challenges we all face through the eyes of a programmer. He recognised early on in his career that the biggest challenge in Life is being happy. And, after much thought, he came up with a formula for happiness

$H = S - F$. *Happiness equals Smiles minus Frowns.*

What does that mean? It means that we need to look for things that make us smile and, whenever something doesn't go our way, we need to remind ourselves not to frown because frowning and despair never help anything. It is more than likely that, as time passes, whatever it was that didn't go our way will be of little consequence.

"It sounds a bit simplistic" I said, but, at the same time, I couldn't deny that there was some logic to Wozniak's theory.

"Actually, Wozniak came up with a second Happiness formula" Greg said. "$H = F3$. Happiness = Food times Fun times Friends. So long as you've got food and friends and you're having fun, you'll be happy."

I could see that there was some truth in Wozniak's second formula too. Both formulae helped explain, at least in part, why people are so happy at Sun Park.

Smiles, friendships, and fun experiences can be found in abundance.

Greg then mentioned a third Happiness formula, this time it was an algorithm inspired by the book *First Things First* written by American author, Stephen Covey. The formula, $H = L4$. "The four L's - living, loving, learning and leaving a legacy - were the foundation for a rich, happy, fulfilling life.

"To Live refers to the physical elements in life" said Greg. "Food, physical health and shelter. The things we need to survive. Physical pleasures are fleeting though. For example, you might enjoy a nice meal, but as soon as you've taken the last bite, it's over.

"To Love covers the emotional dimension of life, a sense of belonging, caring, and connecting. Emotional pleasures come from our relationships with other people. They are far more enduring and more meaningful than any physical pleasure because they affect us on a much deeper level.

"To Learn refers to our intellect; this includes pleasures from learning, understanding and creating.

"Finally, leaving a legacy relates to the spiritual dimension of life. This is where we search for a higher purpose and are driven by the desire to leave a positive legacy for future generations.

"The real problem is that few people ever think about what makes them happy." Greg says. "A few years ago, researchers asked Millennials about their life goals. Over eighty percent said that their major life goal was to get rich. Fifty percent said that their major life goal was to become famous. It seems that most young people still believe that, to be happy, they need to become rich and famous.

"However, it is only as we grow older that we learn through experience what makes us happy and what doesn't. We begin to see past the marketing bullshit."

I agreed, although I wasn't sure where Greg was headed.

"Researchers at Harvard University have been working on what has become the largest study of lifelong happiness." he said. "They studied people from the time they were teenagers all the way into old age to see what really contributes to their health and happiness. For seventy-five years they kept track of the lives of 724 men, year after year they asked them about their work, their home lives, and their health. Of course, the researchers had no way of knowing how the participants' life stories would turn out because studies of this kind, due to their very nature, are exceedingly rare. It isn't uncommon for long-term studies to fail within a decade because, many times, people drop out of the study or funding dries up. Researchers can lose interest or become unwell. Sometimes they die and there's nobody prepared to continue their work.

"The Harvard study, continued over the years. As the participants died or advanced in years, the researchers managed to extend the study to include their children who numbered over 2,000. It is still going on today; every two years the research team contact the participants. They don't just send email surveys, they interview the people in their homes and they are given access to the participants' medical records. They take blood samples, scan the participants' brains, talk to their children, take video recordings of them talking with their wives about their deepest concerns and then they decided to include the wives' in the study too. And, after over seventy-five years of interviews and questionnaires and medical tests, you know what the researchers concluded?"

I shook my head. This was all new to me.

"They concluded the main thing that keeps us happier and healthier throughout our lives is good personal relationships. They had discovered that the quality of our lives really is the quality of our relationships."

"That makes complete sense." I said.

"There were three key lessons highlighted in that study." Greg continued. "The first is that social connections are important for our well-being. People who are more socially connected to family, to friends, and to their community are far happier, healthier, and they tend to live significantly longer than people who have weak social networks.

"The researchers also discovered that the converse is also true. Loneliness is toxic. Being isolated and alone really is a killer. It is a huge issue for society today; the more isolated people become, the less happy they are, and the faster their health declines.

"Here's the key point though; it's not about needing to be around other people because you can feel just as lonely in a crowd as by yourself. And you can be lonely, living with other people, even in a marriage. Which leads to the second big lesson highlighted by the research... it's not the number of friends that we have that's important, it's not whether or not we're in a committed relationship either, because living in the midst of conflict with feelings of resentment and animosity are just as toxic as loneliness."

"What is it about then?"

"It's about the quality of our relationships. That's what matters.

"When the researchers tracked the men's lives back in time from their eighties to age fifty to see if they could have predicted who was going to grow into a happy, healthy octogenarian and who wasn't, they found their answer. They looked at everything about the men's lives and they came to some startling conclusions; there are all kinds of factors that affect our health and happiness, but there was one characteristic that stood out above everything else."

Having spent time at the Green Kitchen I would've guessed that it was related to our diet. But I would've been wrong. "Sure, diet is important." said Greg, "but, it turns out that when you look at people in their fifties, it isn't so much things like their cholesterol levels that predict how happy they will be in later life. It is their personal relationships.

"Incredible as it sounds," said Greg, "researchers are able to accurately predict which individuals in their fifties will be happiest in their eighties simply by reviewing their personal relationships. Those people who are most satisfied with their relationships in their fifties tend to be significantly happier - and healthier for that matter - when they reach their eighties than those who are less satisfied with their relationships in their fifties. What does this mean? Close relationships can act like a shield protecting us from the challenges of aging. Which brings us to the third secret...

"Strong personal relationships don't just protect our bodies, they protect our minds too. Being in a secure relationship with another person in your eighties is healthful. That doesn't mean to say that you must be married or anything like that. You don't even need to be living with someone. What you need is a strong social network, even a handful of true friends, people you feel we can count on in times of need."

I thought about my social network, my family and friends. During my entire married life, it had been my wife who looked after our social life. On a Friday night, I would arrive home and wouldn't have a clue who we were going to see or what we were going to do over the weekend. I think it's a man thing as the situation was the repeated with most other couples in our social circle. But, the consequence of this was that we'd tend to spend our time with her friends and their spouses, and I didn't have a lot in common with many of the husbands. Very few, if any, would I consider a close friend, someone I felt I could count on.

I was in touch with a few old university friends. We shared a history, and I felt a bond when spending time with them. But, would I turn to them for help or advice in a crisis? The truth was I had grown increasingly isolated since my wife's death. I didn't have a large social network, and it was a sobering thought to think that I didn't have a single relationship that would have matched the criteria Greg had described.

Only now was I beginning to formulate an answer to the question Greg had put to me: *"If you were going to invest right now in your future - and I'm not just talking about investing your money, but investing your time and your energy - with the aim of ensuring that your future well-being and happiness would be the very best it could be, what would you do?"*

I smiled. I understood the question and now I also understood the answer. It was simple. "If the key to long-term happiness is close relationships, we all ought to start investing more time and energy into our relationships."

"Exactly!" exclaimed Greg, and he raised his hand to high-five me. "All we really need to be happy are good and loyal friends, loving family and a sense of belonging to a community. What it all boils down to is this; if you want a good life build good relationships."

The value of friendship is something that everyone who comes to Sun Park quickly discovers. Friendship is as pervasive as the sunshine. It is the cornerstone of the ethos and one of the main reasons why people were so happy. Ultimately, people prefer to live in a one-bedroom apartment surrounded by friends than live isolated and alone in a four-bedroom detached house.

CHAPTER 25: ATTITUDE IS EVERYTHING

'Attitude is a little thing that makes a big difference.'
Winston Churchill

Wednesday morning, I walked over the cafe. There was an almighty commotion going on. I could see a lady jabbing her forefinger and shouting at Eddie who was opening the cafe. Then, she turned and, with suitcase in hand, walked out the reception towards the gate.

When I reached the cafe, Eddie was starting up the coffee machine and shaking his head. I ordered an Americano. "What just happened?" I asked.

"Oh, a lady arrived yesterday evening and apparently the toilet in her apartment wasn't working."

"She seemed pretty upset." I said. "That's putting it mildly." smiled Eddie.

"Apparently, it was the final straw for her. She said it was 'unacceptable' that nobody was on reception. I tried to explain that this was a self-service resort and all she needed to do was use the computer over there to report the problem and somebody would be there to sort it out as soon as possible. She asked what she was expected to do in the meantime. And I said, 'well, you could use the wash rooms over there', but she just said that wasn't good enough and stormed out."

"Does that happen a lot?" I asked.

"Not that much anymore," said Eddie. "At the beginning, it was common to see people coming in looking confused. They hadn't really understood the concept and expected to be served as in a standard hotel.

"Last year, a man went to the Marigold one afternoon and complained that there was nobody behind the bar. Apparently, he hadn't realised that it's a self-service resort. Someone explained that the bar is manned on a voluntary basis most evenings, but not twenty-four hours a day. The rest of the time, when nobody is there, he could help himself. I mean, how hard is it to walk behind the bar and get yourself a drink?"

I nodded. Personally, I much preferred helping myself than waiting for someone to serve me.

"Living here," explained Eddie, "is a lot like living at home. Unless, of course, you're super-rich and have a butler or maid waiting on you 24 hours a day. Some people, eh?"

"You can't please everyone." I said with a smile.

"Anyway, as there's no service here" said Eddie, with more than a hint of sarcasm "let me get you that Americano!".

He made the coffee and added a bag of sugar and a caramel biscuit. "If you want to know how other people react when there's a problem, speak to that couple over there." he said.

The couple Eddie was referring to were Cedric, a retired fireman and his wife, Janet. They explained what had happened when they arrived at Sun Park for the first time three years ago. "It wasn't the smoothest of starts," said Cedric. "Our flight had landed at Arrecife airport at 10pm and we didn't get to Sun Park until gone midnight. When we woke in the morning, we discovered that the kettle in our kitchen wasn't working, there was no hot water, and there was only one cup. It was 8:15am and I walked over to the main reception to report the problems.

"I had read the welcome manual which explained that guests should report any maintenance issues via one of the computers in the main reception, which was fine. There is a 'help' button on the main screen that clicks through an online form. You fill in four fields - full name, email address, apartment number and description of problem and click the submit button. Nothing to it really. The issue is logged and sent directly to the maintenance team and then it's just a matter of waiting for someone from maintenance to turn up at the apartment.

"After I had reported the problem, I started to head back to his apartment. As I walked through the main reception and out onto the terrace, I met Melanie, who was sitting drinking coffee and vaping an e-cigarette. I told her about our situation, and she immediately offered to help. 'I live just over there' she said, 'Apartment 606. You're welcome to borrow my kettle. But, if it's just a cup of tea or coffee you're after, I can make one for you and your wife.' I didn't want to put her out, but she insisted."

"A few minutes later, she returned holding two mugs and a small Tupperware containing digestive biscuits.

"I have to say that both I and my wife were so touched by Melanie's kindness and generosity. How often do you meet a total stranger who offers to lend you her kettle and cups or make you and your wife a cup of tea or coffee?

Reflecting on the incident, Cedric believes that the minor issues he and his wife had had with their apartment were a kind of blessing. I asked why and he explained that the whole incident had sparked a special friendship for both him and his wife with Melanie. "I'd never experienced anything like that before. Anywhere." he said. "That's why this place is so special for us. The problems were resolved later that morning, and, by the end of the week, Janet and I had made so many friends that we booked a much longer stay for the following year."

I discovered that Melanie's act of generosity was not an isolated incident. She is by no means the only person to have gone out of their way to help other members of the community. In fact, helping others is commonplace at Sun Park. This is because people look upon helping others as an opportunity to boost their own happiness and well-being. Looking out for others is a very large and key part of the ethos.

Most people, out in the real world, are out for themselves. They are on a quest to acquire more things for themselves and their family. Bigger houses, faster cars, the latest gadgets, and the latest fashions, new clothes (much of which they'll never even wear). At Sun Park, there is an entirely different ethos; the main quest is to acquire friendships and experiences. People look to contribute, and they help their neighbours and friends wherever possible. Psychologists refer to this as performing random acts of kindness. I googled it during my stay. Doing something for someone else without expectation of reward has been shown to be one of the most effective ways of increasing our own levels of happiness in life. The act itself is not important. It can be as trivial as holding a door open for someone, or listening to their problems. But, whatever the act is, doing it just because you can and with no ulterior motive brings its own rewards.

Random acts of kindness make us feel good about ourselves. They raise our self-esteem as well as our feelings of happiness in a way that nothing else can rival. Any feelings of pride in acquiring something like a new watch or a new pair of shoes quickly fades, and pales into insignificance next to the joy experienced through helping someone in need.

There are a multitude of heart-warming stories involving random acts of kindness at Sun Park. When Veronica and Don needed to install special facilities in their apartment a few months after they had decided to make Sun Park their second home. Don, who is wheelchair bound due to Multiple Sclerosis, needed extra fittings in the bathroom to be able to get in and out of the shower. They ordered the fittings online and, the day they arrived, word got around and volunteers were literally queueing up to help.

The most touching story I heard was one that involved the entire community who joined together and, with selfless love and compassion, helped save a man's life. That man was Alfred and, when I met him during the week, I discovered the depth of the community spirit at Sun Park is nothing short of remarkable.

~

Every now and again at Sun Park, if you listen very carefully, you'll notice a strange melody in the air. Musical notes, carried on the breeze. Five tones repeated in sequence: d e c C G. I recognise the tune from the 1977 Blockbuster movie 'Close Encounters of The Third Kind'. The first time I heard it I was sitting on my terrace one afternoon reading the news on my iPad. Initially, I thought a video was playing on the iPad. Then I realised that the melody was coming from somewhere on the resort. Later, around tea time, I heard it again. I asked my neighbour Joyce who was sitting out on her terrace.

Joyce is one of those people who seem to be always smiling, always happy. She is a widow from Sussex, a small lady no taller than five feet, with a bob haircut. From a distance, you might easily mistake her for a schoolgirl. Joyce was staying at Sun Park for the third time. She comes by herself because she's made so many friends at Sun Park that, each time she arrives, there is a welcoming crowd to greet her. "It is amazing," she said. "I'd been away for nearly nine months and as I arrived at the gate, my friends May and Judith were right there waiting for me. I was so touched that I wanted to cry."

I asked Joyce if she knew what the noise was and where it was coming from "What noise?" she said.

I whistled the tune. "Da Daa Da Daaa Da".

"Ah. You mean Chuck!" she said with a grin. "You haven't met him yet?"

"No. Who's Chuck?" I said.

"He's Alfred's flatmate." she replied.

"Alfred?"

"Yes. He and Chuck - his parrot - live three doors down."

"Ah...Now it makes sense." I said.

Joyce explained that several months earlier, Alfred had had a stroke. He had been in his apartment at the time, but had managed to crawl to the front door, which was open. Alfred's neighbour heard him fall, and within minutes, a group of members took control of the situation. One called an ambulance, another placed a pillow under Alfred's head. A cool damp towel placed on his forehead and Melanie, who is a trained nurse, was holding Alfred's hand and reassuring him that he was going to be fine. Melanie told Jeannie to write down all the medications that were in the apartment. Jeannie checked the bedroom, bathroom cabinet and kitchen cupboards and noted all the medications she could find.

After an acute stroke, time is of the essence. This is because the affected area of the brain is being starved of blood. Brain cells start dying. It is a race against time. The sooner a person suffering a stroke gets to an emergency room, the more likely it is that blood flow to the affected area of the brain will be restored which saves brain cells. The more brain cells that can be saved, the better the chances are for a good and speedy recovery.

Alfred was lucky. Lucky that he wasn't sitting alone in a house on the edge of a housing estate in Kent where nobody would have heard his cries. He'd lived in that house for some twenty years. Other than to say, 'Good morning' on the odd occasion that they'd cross paths, Alfred didn't know any of his neighbours in the UK. And, like me, after his wife had passed away, he had spent most evenings sitting alone in his home watching the TV. Had he suffered a stroke whilst living in that house, the chances are he would have died.

Fortunately, when the stroke erupted, Alfred was surrounded, not just by people, but by friends. He was looked after, and help came quickly. Within minutes, an ambulance had arrived, and Alfred was taken to the local hospital for treatment that saved his life. Once in a stable condition, he was transferred to a hospital on the neighbouring, larger island of Gran Canaria. Greg and Christina made regular visits to the hospital to check up on Alfred, and two months later he was allowed to return to Sun Park, but on the proviso, that he attended daily therapy to complete his recovery. This produced a dilemma. Sun Park is for active over-50s, it isn't a care home. But, in this instance, everyone agreed; Alfred was a member of the community and the doctors had said that there was no reason why he shouldn't recover. He may not be able to return to his former self, but all the signs suggested that he would be able to regain a fully independent life and be able to care for himself. So, a nurse came in each day to take him to his daily therapy, and in the evenings, Alfred's friends took turns to sit with him.

When I met Alfred, it had been over six months since his stroke. He could stand and walk with the aid of a stick, and although his speech was slow and slightly slurred at times, he could converse fairly. Despite his ordeal, or possibly because of it, Alfred maintained a cheerful disposition. Perhaps it was due to him being aware of how close he had come to dying, or the overwhelming gratitude he felt towards everyone who had looked after him, that made his recovery possible.

The morning I met Alfred, Chuck was whistling his tune again. I was walking back to my apartment and the melody was quite a bit louder than I had heard from my apartment. I stopped and looked around and noticed a man looking slightly frail and tired, sitting on his terrace. A book and a cup of coffee were on the table in front of him. The door to his apartment was open and I could see a large bird cage inside. "So, that's the famous Chuck?" I said.

"Ay, it is." said Alfred.

I introduced myself and Alfred leaned forward to offer his hand. "Want t'meet him?", he said.

"Sure!". I'd never been up close to a live singing parrot before.

"Hang on a sec." said Alfred, "and I'll bring him out." Alfred slowly raised himself out of his chair and shuffled with the aid of a walking stick into his apartment. A moment later he was back, pushing a large bird cage on wheels. Chuck was perched on top of the cage. "This is Chuck." he said with pride. "Chuck meet Stan".

Chuck turned out to be a Blue-Fronted Amazon parrot distinguished by the bright aqua marine markings on its head. His body was covered with bright yellow and green feathers. Alfred explained that these parrots were highly intelligent. "Chuck's a very, very smart cookie." he said.

"I'm a smart cookie! I'm a smart cookie!" screamed Chuck, right on cue.

"Chuck can mimic human voices and sounds better than any TV impressionist." Alfred said with a wink. "He can talk for hours and hours too, though that's not always a good thing. Best of all, he can sing."

Alfred turned to Chuck and said. "Are you lonely, Chuck?" and immediately Chuck began singing the first bar of the song.

I smiled. "Did you train him to do that?" I asked.

"Not really" said Alfred. "I was playing some songs by Elvis Presley and Chuck kind of picked it up from there."

"Does he sing other songs?"

"Yes. And he doesn't just sing, he's very affectionate too."

I had read, long ago, that some parrots form deep and lasting relationships with humans but, in many cases, they develop a special bond with just one person. Being a highly intelligent bird, Chuck thrived on social interaction. Alfred told me he and Chuck had been companions for over fifteen years but that meant that Chuck would, in all probability, outlive Alfred by decades as the typical lifespan of these birds was said to be in the region of eighty years or more.

"I used to worry about what would happen to Chuck after I'm gone," said Alfred. "Sure, he'll miss me, but I know that, for as long as Sun Park is here, my Chuck will be well cared for."

I thought about what Alfred had said. My biggest fear about dying had always been concern for the people I would leave behind. You just want some reassurance that they'll be alright. The job of a being a parent is not to give a child everything he or she needs, but to help them fend for themselves. I was happy in the knowledge that, as far as my kids were concerned, my job was done.

Alfred offered me a drink. I accepted a glass of water and sat down with him and Chuck on his terrace. I learned that Alfred is one of the people who had chosen to make Sun Park his second home. Like many others, he turned up on a Social Friday, and booked to come over for a taster week. He said he knew the very first day that this was where he wanted to be.

I smiled. "That's understandable." I said. I gestured to the swimming pools and surrounding gardens. "Why would anyone not want to stay here?"

"It wasn't just how lovely Sun Park is," he said. "Nor was it the beautiful location or this glorious weather," he said. "It was the community spirit here, or what we call 'the ethos'."

Everyone spoke about the wonderful ethos, but I was curious to understand what it meant to Alfred. Although I had heard his story from Joyce the previous day, it was interesting hearing a first-hand account. "I thought I was going to die." Alfred said. "It all happened so quickly. One minute I was fine, then I felt dizzy and collapsed. Right in there," he said pointing inside the door of this apartment. "Then there were people all around me and the next thing I remember was waking up in hospital.

"I know I'm lucky to be alive," he said. "If I'd been back at home by myself in the UK, I'd probably be dead. The only reason why I'm sitting here today is because of the amazing friends I have here. They mean everything to me. They saved my life."

CHAPTER 26: THE SIXTH BLUE ZONE

*'Friendship marks a life even more deeply than love.
Love risks degenerating into obsession, friendship is
never anything but sharing.'*
Elie Wiesel

Mark is an award-winning travel writer. He specialises in reviewing travel destinations for the over fifties market. Writing was his second career. It was after being retired off from the Police force in his mid-sixties, that Mark started writing. He submitted a few short articles and, to his delight, discovered that the editors liked his style. Since that time, which was a little over a decade ago, he has travelled around the world visiting a wide range of resorts and holiday destinations. If you want to know anything about the needs of mature travellers, Mark is your man.

I met Mark playing Pétanque one afternoon. Pétanque (otherwise known as boules) is a fun game and relatively easy to play. It's one of those inclusive games that virtually anyone can play. If you can throw a ball that is similar in size and weight to a cricket ball, you can play Pétanque. Strength and agility don't enter into it. The key is having good spatial awareness and an aptitude for throwing the ball as close to the jack (a smaller white ball) as possible. It is usually played in teams, which is exactly how we like to play it. As many as four players per team and you can have two or three teams playing against each other in the same game.

Playing games like Pétanque is a great way to get to know a lot of people in a short space of time. I tried to speak to as many people at Sun Park as I could because I was particularly interested to know their stories: Who were they? What had attracted them to Sun Park? And why did they choose to keep coming back year after year?

After the game, the players usually enjoy a cold drink together, either at the Ching Ching Chiringuito bar, because it is next to the Pétanque court, or sometimes up at the cafe in the main reception. That afternoon we chose to congregate at the Chiringuito and I ended up sitting next to Mark. I asked him why he had come to Sun Park.

"Why am I here?" Mark said. "That's a good question. I first came here three years ago to write a review for Silver Travel." Mark explained that Silver Travel was not a travel agency. It was a review site which is to say that it reviews holidays and travel destinations for the over-fifties market.

"Unlike many people who come here," Mark said, "I didn't know what to expect. I didn't read anything or watch any videos. I didn't even look at a brochure."

"Why not?"

"Well, I do the same everywhere I go. If I'm reviewing a destination, I don't want to arrive with any preconceived ideas. You know?"

I nodded. That notion is honourable for a travel writer although I wouldn't think it would be wise for a paying customer to arrive at any hotel or resort without knowing anything about where they were going. In fact, I imagine that coming to a place like Sun Park without understanding what it was and how it worked could lead to frustration and disappointment. Many people, including Greg, had said the same thing. On the rare occasion when people had booked without taking the time to review the facilities and understand the ethos, invariably the start of their stay had not been a happy one. I mentioned this to Mark and he totally agreed. "It is when people's expectations don't match their experience that most problems occur. But, in my case, being a travel writer, I like to arrive free from any prejudice or judgement.

"To be frank, I wasn't sure that I'd enjoy it. I didn't know what to expect, but I quickly discovered that it's unlike anything else I've experienced. Really! I've never been anywhere quite like Sun Park. It's not a traditional hotel and it is not your typical self-service aparthotel either.

"What I love about this place is that it offers a totally unique experience. For people of our age, active and over fifty years of age, Sun Park is almost revolutionary. I mean, to come and live in the sun in such a spectacular location is amazing by itself. But, after my first week, having experienced the ethos here, I was totally blown away.

"There is something about Sun Park that brings out the best in people. I realised that it is less to do with the sunshine and weather than it is to do with the people and the community spirit. There's a wonderful atmosphere here.

"On top of the friendliness, there are so many things to do...art classes, walking, cycling, yoga, days out...you don't get a holiday here, you get a life experience! It's a fantastic way to live.

"You know what Sun Park is to me?", he said. "It is the sixth Blue Zone!"

I'd never heard of Blue Zones and asked what they were.

"The Blue Zones are where you go if you want to live a long, happy and healthy life!" he said. "Come with me. Let me show you."

Mark led me into the library at the back of the reception and pulled a book off the top shelf. 'Blue Zones' by Dan Buettner. I looked at the back cover. *'A long, healthy life is no accident. It begins with good genes, but it also depends on good habits. If you adopt the right lifestyle, experts say, chances are you may live up to a decade longer.'* Further down it read, *'Buettner has led teams of researchers across the globe - from Costa Rica to Sardinia, Italy, to Okinawa, Japan and beyond - to uncover the secrets of Blue Zones. He found that the recipe for longevity is deeply intertwined with community, lifestyle, and spirituality.'*

"This looks fascinating." I said.

Mark smiled. "That's exactly what it is." he said. "You'll enjoy it, I'm sure."

He looked at his watch. "I'll have to leave you to discover the Blue Zones. My wife and I are going out soon."

"Sure. Have a good time. And, thanks for this." I replied holding up the book.

I took a bottle of water and walked out onto the terrace and began to read.

~

The story of the Blue Zones was first told in the November 2005 edition of National Geographic Magazine. The cover story, 'The Secrets of a Long Life', written by Dan Buettner, revealed the secrets of longevity based upon his team's research into five distinct geographical areas around the world where people tend to live much longer, happier, healthier lives than other populations. The areas included Okinawa (Japan), Sardinia (Italy), Nicoya (Costa Rica), Icaria (Greece) and last, but not least, the Seventh Day Adventist community in Loma Linda (California, USA).

The term 'Blue Zones' wasn't related to the oceans or water, as I had initially thought. It came from the work of other longevity researchers, Gianni Pes and Michel Poulain, which had appeared earlier in the *Journal of Experimental Gerontology*. It was Pes and Poulain who had first identified Sardinia's Nuoro province as the region with the highest concentration of male centenarians, and they had marked the cluster of villages that had the highest longevity by drawing concentric blue circles around them. Those circles became known as the 'Blue Zones'. Buettner and his team had looked for other regions around the world that showed similar longevity patterns, and their search led them to four more Blue Zones.

Longevity wasn't something about which I had ever given great thought. There had been a brief period, a long time ago when, as a young boy of eleven or twelve years of age, I became anxious about the shortness of life. We were told in Bible study that the age of man was 'three score years and ten'. That meant, if I was lucky, I could look forward to another fifty-eight summers and Xmas holidays! That sombre thought quickly left me and I never thought about the brevity of life again. Until very recently. Absurd as it sounds now, I had never really considered how my lifestyle might influence the length and quality of my life. Or, had I been too busy to care?

Frankly, I had no interest in living to be a centenarian. People might be living longer but, looking around at my older relatives and others of their age, I had no desire to live a longer life if that meant being in a state of comparative ill-health and dependence and, dare I say it, senility and decrepitude. But, if it were possible to extend quality of life with those extra years, then that might be something worth aspiring to.

The Blue Zones weren't about just extending life, they were about extending quality of life too. They promised to reveal the habits and characteristics of people who didn't just live long lives, they lived long, happy and healthy lives. So, what were their secrets? Why did the people living in these Blue Zones live significantly healthier, happier and longer lives than the rest of us?

Reading the book, I learned that Buettner and his team of researchers visited the communities in the Blue Zones to observe for themselves how the people lived. In addition, they collated and analysed all the empirical and epidemiological data to help them better understand the reasons behind the success of the Blue Zone communities, and they came to some startling conclusions.

The Blue Zones all differ in terms of geography. What these communities shared were common lifestyle choices, and these, according to Buettner, were the predominant drivers contributing to their longevity. The people living in Blue Zones were, by and large, non-smokers, they drank very moderate amounts of alcohol by many standards (sticking mainly to organic wine). They engaged in moderate, daily physical activity, and they ate largely plant-based, low calorie diets. These were all factors that any reputable health researcher would have expected. Who is not aware that cigarettes and excess alcohol damage our health? And, as I had learned during my time at Sun Park, the positive impact of a plant-based diet and physical exercise on our health and well-being has been corroborated by a wealth of clinical and epidemiological research over recent decades. However, other shared characteristics of the Blue Zone communities began to emerge that were not quite so obvious.

Some of the most important lessons from the Blue Zones was the way in which family and friendship were highly valued. There were exceedingly high levels of social engagement in all the Blue Zone communities. Interestingly, everything is easily accessible in the Blue Zones. Just as Richard Dunston had described his home town Wolverston, everywhere in the Blue Zones is within walking distance.

Buettner also observed that everyone, regardless of age, was socially active and integrated in the community. The concept of retirement, the very word, is unheard of in the Blue Zones. Everyone is regarded as a productive member of the community. They all live with a common purpose that gives their lives direction and meaning. This was particularly evident in Okinawa where the ethos is based upon 'Moai' (pronounced Mow-wee), a concept that holds one of most important keys to successful longevity, shared life experiences.

Literally translated Moai means "meeting for a common purpose". The Okinawans endow a sense of Moai in the community from a young age. They gather their children into groups of five or more and encourage them to stay together as a group through their journey in life. Nobody is left alone. There is no feeling of isolation which, researchers have discovered, is as toxic and harmful to our health as smoking a pack of cigarettes. In a Moai, every member of the group supports the others, and they share in each other's fortunes and misfortunes throughout their lives.

Buettner found some Moais, small friendship groups, that were still thriving after nine decades. Women centenarians still worked and played together. They shared meals, drank wine, argued about the past, and shared their dreams for the future. In Moais, people stick together through their joys and disappointments, and the result is that they multiply their happiness and better endure hardship and sadness. And, throughout it all, they enjoy significantly healthier and considerably longer lives than everyone else.

The more I reflected on the Blue Zones, the more I could see parallels with the ethos of the community at Sun Park. The layout of Sun Park played a large part. As in the Blue Zones, everything was easily accessible. Your friends are your neighbours. Even those who might be staying at the other end of the resort are no more than a short walk away. The same can be said of the facilities; the bars, the laundry, the shops, the activities, and the health centre are all there on site. Nothing is so far away that it can't be reached by walking.

Another similarity between the Blue Zones and Sun Park is shared values. Moais occurred naturally, without any force or direction, at Sun Park. They were the inevitable outcome of an ethos that encouraged friendship. However, the Moais at Sun Park are dynamic and evolving. Unlike tribal groups which tend to be restricted to members of the tribe, the Moais at Sun Park are more akin to friendship groups that embrace everyone. The groups tend to be formed through shared activities and interests, and through working together on group or community projects.

The real power of the Moai is that it brings people together in a circle of friendship that lasts a lifetime. In Sun Park, as in the Blue Zones, the Moai is central to the community and to the ethos. Nothing is as highly prized as friendship. This may explain why so many people return to Sun Park, year after year. They keep coming back because it is the home of their Moai, a place where they feel a sense of belonging that is unaffected by distance and time.

CHAPTER 27: KEEP LOVE IN YOUR HEART

'Keep love in your heart. A life without it is like a sunless garden when the flowers are dead.'
Oscar Wilde

10:30pm. Thursday evening. I'm sitting at the Ching-Ching Chiringuito bar sharing a bottle of vino tinto with some new friends. Although it is February, on Lanzarote it is still warm enough to sit outside wearing jeans and a sweater. We're on our second bottle and talking about love and relationships. One of the women in the group, Karin, a woman who has been single for the past four years, asks "Where do men go to meet women these days?"

It's a good question. I confess to the group that I joined a few dating apps. Swipe right for a match and left for 'no thanks'. "It might work for some," I said, "but it didn't work for me."

Andrew, a musician from Stockport, agreed. "I read a report that examined more than 19 million messages from over 400,000 single people within a well-known dating app," he says, "and it transpired that over half of all the messages never received a reply!"

"And, even if you do get a reply, you'll probably be chatting with a robot." Steve, an engineer from Manchester pitches in.

"You mean a chatbot?" I ask.

"What's a chatbot?" says Karin.

"A chatbot is a computer program that responds like a person," I say. "A bit like the Alexa in reception, but done through a messaging interface. They are becoming increasingly common. My old company used them in customer service."

"Exactly!" says Andrew. "A few years ago, a well-known dating app was found to be full of fake female profiles and the site deployed chat bots to lure single men."

I vaguely remembered reading about that. It was quite a scandal at the time. Over eighty percent of male customers thought they were messaging single women, but it turned out that they were really talking to chat bots! Crazy, huh?"

"Online dating didn't work for me either," says Karin. I am surprised because Karin is a head turner; very attractive; slim, sporty, blonde, bright blue eyes, and a beautiful smile. I couldn't imagine anyone not swiping to the right when they saw her profile. She explains that it was exhausting filtering and messaging contacts, only to find that the few men she dated were almost unrecognisable from their online profiles. "Why do people do that?" she says.

Andrew takes out his phone and asks Google. "How do men and women meet these days?" There's nothing Google doesn't know. "This is interesting," he says. "Most people find their spouse, or significant other, through one of four ways. In fourth spot is a 'personal introduction' by a friend or family member. Less than ten percent of all marriages start this way so the chances of success aren't high.

"Next up, in third spot, is... a night out at a bar or nightclub. Not a great bet, it would seem, because, again, the chances of it ending up in a long-term relationship are very small."

"That doesn't surprise me," says Karin.

"Me neither." I add.

"In second spot," continues Andrew, "with a much higher success rate is... meeting in the workplace or college. Apparently, twenty percent of long-term relationships begin with an office romance."

"I'll have to find another office job then." I say.

"Not so fast, Stan," says Andrew. "In top spot, with higher success than the others combined is...drumroll... a shared interest and life experience."

"Shared activities and experiences?" Karin says. "Of course! That makes sense."

"A hundred percent!" I say.

Karin makes a good point. Perhaps the reason I haven't met a woman back in the UK is that I don't have any hobbies or special interests. There's no activity that I'm passionate about. For more years than I care to remember, my life has revolved around family and work. There hasn't been time for much else. Or, is that just an excuse?

"I think that's one of the great things about Sun Park." Karin says. "I've tried more activities here in the last week than I've done back at home in the past year!"

I admit that my experience has been the same. "I don't get out enough at home," I say, "mainly because I'm so exhausted by the time I get home from work."

"I think we're all in the same boat." says Steve. "It isn't easy. I think you've got to make the effort."

"If you find something you really love doing and you like the people you're doing it with, I think you'll find the time." says Karin.

"I think that's one reason why I am enjoying being here so much." I say. "There's no shortage of activities to try, or people to do them with."

Just then, as if on cue, a couple walk by holding hands. Andrew calls out to them. "Good evening!". Their names are Dan and Betty. Dan is a former sales rep for IBM and Betty is a hairdresser. They met here at Sun Park. Both were keen cyclists and got to know each other on one of the group cycling trips. "There are maybe a dozen of us who go out most mornings," says Dan, "sometimes along the coast, and other times we go inland."

"Inland is a lot harder," says Betty, "because it gets hilly."

"That's true." says Dan. "But, we all go at a comfortable pace and we always stop somewhere for a coffee along the way."

"I wouldn't mind going cycling." says Karin.

"I'd be up for that too." I add. I had a bicycle many years ago. I remember putting a child's seat on the back and cycling in the park, my son on the back of my bike and my daughter, being a few years older, riding her own bike in front of us. Happy times! Whatever happened to that bike? Why did I stop cycling?

"Why don't you come along with us one day?" says Dan. "The times are all on the noticeboard."

"Sounds good." I said. "I haven't been on a bicycle for years."

"Me neither." says Karin.

"Come tomorrow then," says Betty. "We're going along the coast. It's a very easy ride. Plus, there's a fabulous place we stop for coffee."

"You've sold it to me." I say. "I'm in."

"Me too," Karin says and she smiles at me. I don't know if she's flirting. I've been in the wilderness for too long to gauge a woman's intentions. But, for now, I'm happy just to have made a female friend. Who knows where it will lead?

Andrew and Steve pass. Andrew says he'll stick with hiking, and Steve is going home in a few days and has pretty much filled up his diary for the rest of his stay.

"Where can we get bikes?" I ask.

"No worries there," says Dan, "There is a collection of bicycles and helmets available for anyone to use."

"Thanks, sounds great." I say.

"It will be," says Dan. "We'll see you both in the morning. 10:00am in reception.

~

Lying in bed that night I'm feeling excited. I think I've discovered one of the secrets of Sun Park and the reason why being active is such a key part of the ethos. These 'intentional activities' are the key, not just to a happier, more fulfilling life, but also to forming friendships. Maybe even to finding a life partner? It is obvious to me now that family and work, and sitting indoors watching TV, isn't enough. I promise myself that when I'm back in the UK, I'll get out more and be more active. I'll start by joining local Tai Chi and Dance classes. I'd already decided to join a local Bridge Club too, so those should all be a good start. The thought excited me. I am more determined than ever to take advantage of the activities on offer during my remaining time here at Sun Park. I'm looking forward to getting back on a bike and cycling with Karin and the rest of the group along the island's coast.

~

11:30am. I'm with Karin and a group of fellow cyclists sitting in a small cafe, right on the seafront, somewhere along the coast. We cycled just under ten kilometres in forty minutes and I must say I haven't had so much fun in a very long time. The boardwalk is wide and mostly flat, just as Dan had described. We pedalled along the shore under a clear, blue sky - no cars, no fumes, no traffic - just bright sunshine and a light, cool sea breeze. The experience is...liberating. Comparable to skiing down a mountain in the Pyrenese. You feel totally carefree and happy to be alive. I can't believe that it's taken me to come here to rediscover this simple pleasure.

Karin and I continued from where we left off the night before. I discovered we had a lot in common. She had lost her husband to prostate cancer six years ago. He'd never had a well man check-up and by the time cancer was diagnosed, it was too late. She had two daughters, two years apart, both of whom were at university. It was when her elder daughter went travelling in her gap year that Karin had decided to see more of the world herself. Travelling as a lone woman isn't easy at any age, and she'd gone a few 'solos' trips, the ones specifically designed for singles. "They were fun," she said, "but a few months ago, a friend had recommended Sun Park. And here I am."

"What are your initial impressions?" I asked.

"I'm really enjoying myself." she said. "What about you?"

"You know something," I said, "coming here has been one of the best things I've done since my wife passed away. I came out to Lanzarote a few weeks ago and all I was thinking about was having a holiday; you know, have a rest, sunshine, read a book... but this has been much more. I've made so many new friends, I've learned a lot about myself, I've tried new activities. Like today, riding a bike. I haven't been on a bike for over twenty years! Don't ask me why!"

"I know exactly what you mean," Karin said. "I feel the same way. I don't know what it is either. I've been to holiday resorts before so it isn't just about the weather. There's something about the community spirit here..."

"The ethos?"

"Yes! The ethos. It makes you feel... part of something."

I nodded. Part of something. Connected. For so many years, I've been alone. From the moment I walked through the gates at Sun Park, I felt connected. Among friends. Part of a community. Now, I am sitting with a bunch of new friends and having a real conversation with a beautiful woman. When was the last time I did that?

Ten minutes later we are all back on our bikes, cycling along the promenade. Fishing boats and a couple of yachts are gliding across the sea. The sun is shining. There is a cool, refreshing sea breeze. I feel something unfamiliar. I can't describe it, it's a feeling of being at peace, complete contentment.

Happiness? No, it's even more than that. I feel love...for this place, for this moment, for the people I'm with. I haven't said or thought this in a very long time... right now, I love my life.

CHAPTER 28: GOODNIGHT ELVIS

*'You've gotta dance like there's nobody watching,
love like you'll never be hurt, sing like there's
nobody listening, and live like it's heaven on earth.'*
William W. Purkey

Once a month, Jack Chapstone, a singer from Sheffield puts on a bouffant rock'n'roll wig, classic retro sunglasses, a white polyester jump suit with the widest flared trousers I've ever seen, and a red shirt unbuttoned to his navel. As soon as he walks out onto the stage in the Marigold Bar, Jack has the crowd in the palm of his hand. Before he reaches the first chorus of *The Green Green Grass of Home*, almost everyone in the audience is on their feet. The bar is never busier, the room is never livelier, and the people are never buzzing with as much energy as on Elvis Night.

Underneath the garb and the spray tan, Jack is a balding, pale, freckled man in his early sixties. He spent over twenty-five years trudging around the pubs and clubs of North Yorkshire impersonating the musical legends; Frank Sinatra, Neil Diamond, and Johnny Cash were just a few of his alter personas. However, by far the most popular among his repertoire is Elvis, The King of Rock 'n Roll, and it is as Elvis that Jack returns, time and again, to entertain the members and guests at Sun Park.

I've not met a Yorkshireman yet who can pull off the Memphis twang that Elvis made his own, and I found it hard not to be amused by a man with a beer belly and a hip replacement trying to emulate the Elvis pelvic thrust. That said, there was no denying that Jack is an accomplished entertainer. He doesn't hit a bum note and, to give him his dues, he had the entire place rocking.

A week ago, these people were all strangers to me. Now, many were my friends. George, the man who had stayed up past midnight to welcome me on my first night, was dancing with his wife, Evelyn. Jim and Pippa were gliding around the dance floor in what I'm told is American Smooth, a type of ballroom dancing. Jim's daughters, Kirsty and Krystal, were doing the Ceroc moves we had learned at the dance class earlier in the week. Joel was there too, looking like a professional, jive dancing with Sandy, who was herself a former professional dancer. One woman took Jonathan, the man who was on his first vacation in eight years, by the hand and, overcoming his initial protestations, led him smiling onto the dance floor.

Michael, the Scotsman who had only intended to stay for five days, was there as well. Being at least half a head taller than most of the others made Michael hard to miss, but the transformation in him since I'd first met him at Barney's on the previous Friday night was astonishing. He was among a small group of people standing by the bar, and he looked in his element. Our eyes met briefly. I held my thumb up and he responded with the 'a-okay' gesture. Michael had changed from a shy, awkward and introverted man into someone who appeared confident and at ease. He was chatting animatedly and seemed to be thoroughly enjoying himself. I discovered later that Michael had extended his stay by a further three weeks. I asked him why, and he said: "Because when you've had the best time of your life, you don't want it to stop."

Out of the corner of my eye I noticed Roy and his pal, Sid, starting a conga line. One by one people joined the line as it wove around the dance floor and then passed in front of the bar and through the tables. As the line moved in front of me, a space suddenly appeared. Karin grabbed my hand and placed it on the back of her hip, pulling me into the ever-expanding line.

That moment has stayed with me ever since. It captured the very essence of the ethos. Life's for living, for being, not for sitting on the side-lines watching everything pass you by. Just as it's more fun being part a conga than standing around watching it pass by, life is much more fun, we're happier and healthier, when we get involved and connect to the people around us.

I have lived for sixty years and it is only now, after coming to Sun Park, that I fully appreciate that the difference between living an ordinary life and an extraordinary life is not about wealth or fame or personal achievements. It's not about the material things, the house we live in, the car we drive, or how much money we have. The one thing that matters above all else is friendship. The quality of our lives really does come down to the quality of our relationships.

As I danced with the others around the hall that night, just one among many, I remember thinking that this is what life is about; being part of a wonderful community. This is where the magic happens in Life.

Chapter 29: Saying Goodbye

'Saying goodbye doesn't mean anything.
It's the time we spent together that matters,
not how we left it.'
Trey Parker

Goodbyes are never easy. Especially when you don't know if, or when, you'll ever meet again. Perhaps we would meet again, but I knew that if we did, it wouldn't be here. There would be no return from the journey I was about to make.

Blue skies. Bright sunshine. The sound of laughter and music fills the air. But, when the music stopped, I knew it was time to say 'goodbye'. One by one, I bid my farewells. There were no words said. None were needed. Just warm handshakes, hugs and kisses.

As I passed through the main gate for the last time, the emotion of the event became overwhelming. I fought hard without success to hold back tears. They were tears of sadness at having to leave the place I called home and the people I counted among my closest friends. But, there were also tears of gratitude and love. For being reborn, for nearly three decades of love and friendship and adventure that I would not have known had it not been for this remarkable place and the many wonderful friends I made here.

Here I found the four L's - the importance of living, loving, learning and leaving a legacy. I had lived every minute of every day, mindful that the present moment is a gift, it is all we have. During the years at Sun Park, I had loved and been loved; by friends and family, and by one wonderful woman whose recent passing left me heartbroken. I'm not sure how I would have coped with that loss without the love and support of my friends. I had learned so much and grown as a person, and I hoped that I had touched the lives of the people as much as they had touched mine. Perhaps that is the greatest legacy we can leave.

Lanzarote is sometimes referred to as 'second chance island' because, out of the devastation of volcanic eruptions, the island was itself reborn. The island represents second chances in life, and it lived up to that promise for me.

Now, it was time to leave. Outside the main gates of the resort, I hugged my friends and said, 'good bye' for the last time.

I had arrived at Sun Park with a single suitcase and I left twenty-seven years later with the same suitcase. Whatever possessions I owned, a few kitchen appliances and some pieces of furniture, I left for my friends. I wouldn't need those or much else where I was going.

When I walked through the gates at Sun Park, I had come with no expectations. I had lost my job; my career, if you can call it a career, was over. I had few friends and no social life to speak of. Worst of all, I was fearful of the future. My initial visit to Lanzarote had been impetuous. A quick, impulsive decision driven by a desire to get away. Then, one day, by some stroke of luck, some might call it Providence, I walked down a road and past the entrance of Sun Park. I could just as easily have walked down the previous turning or the subsequent one. But, I am sure of this; had I not found Sun Park, I would have missed out on the friendship, happiness and love that I experienced during the last twenty-seven years of my life.

When I came to Sun Park, my intention was to stay for just a week, but that week turned into a month, the month turned into a year, and the year turned into nearly three decades. Why did I stay? It's true that I loved living in a warm climate, by the sea, in one of the most beautiful parts of one of the most beautiful islands in the Western hemisphere. But that, of itself, wasn't why I decided to stay at Sun Park.

I stayed because I was reborn. I found a new life, and new friends. I stayed because I was embraced and made welcome by everyone. I stayed because I felt that this was 'home', where I belonged. But, most of all, I stayed because of the ethos.

Though I was leaving Sun Park, I knew that Sun Park would never leave me. Ultimately, the ethos I had found and had tried to live my life by, is not confined to the walls that surrounded the resort. The ethos comes from the people and, once it touches you, it becomes part of you. It is like a guiding spirit supporting you, wherever life may lead.

EPILOGUE

'The fear of death follows from the fear of life.
A man who lives fully is prepared to die at any time.'
Mark Twain

There is a tale in Chinese folklore of a young man who had learned of a place called 'Paradise Island'. According to legend, the moment a person arrives at the island, they feel at one with the Universe, and experience pure joy and happiness in their hearts. The island was far away from the young man's village and the journey was said to be treacherous, accessed only by climbing a mountain so high it touches the clouds, traversing rivers that roar like thunder, passing through rainforests so dense you cannot see beyond each step, and sailing the Great Sea where waves rise higher than ten oak trees.

According to the ancient texts, the journey was so arduous that it could take months, perhaps years. However, the young man was determined. He did little else but work, eat and sleep, preparing himself for the journey. He thought of nothing else. He had no time for friends or frivolity, and no thought for love and companionship. Although, with each passing year, he grew lonelier and more dissatisfied with his life, comforted only by the knowledge that, one day, he would be in Paradise and there he would surely know pure joy and happiness.

Finally, on a cold, winter's day, he set off. He knew that, if he delayed the journey any longer, he would soon be too old and too frail to travel. Having kept himself to himself for so many years, there was nobody to bid him farewell. No family or friends to wave 'goodbye'. He left in the quiet of dawn, alone, determined to find the island and to experience the pure joy and happiness that awaited.

The journey proved more difficult than the man had ever imagined. It took many years to successfully climb the mountain, cross the rivers, hack his way, step by step, through the rainforests, and sail through one hundred-foot waves over the Great Sea until, at last, he reached Paradise.

Stepping off his boat, physically and emotionally exhausted, the man was surprised not to feel the pure joy and happiness that the ancient texts had promised. He saw an old Sage sitting on the beach.

"Is this Paradise?" the man asked the Sage.

"Yes, it is."

"When will I feel joy or happiness?" said the man.

"Joy and happiness, my friend, are found in the journey," said the Sage, "not the destination."

~

It was in the middle of the night that I shut my eyes for the last time. The timing could have been better. If I had written the script, my heart would have remained beating for just a few hours longer. My children and grandchildren would have been with me at my bedside. Does it matter? Probably not. They were in my heart and my thoughts to the end. I hope I was in theirs too. They are a large part of what made my life worth having been lived.

I could sense the end of my journey was approaching. I saw my life in a dream, although far more real. I knew that I could have done more, become more. Certainly, I could have achieved more. But, when all is said and done, would it have made any difference to me or to the world if I had?

More important than unfulfilled achievement is the question of unfulfilled potential. Could I have been truer to myself? Might I have been happier? Was my life meaningful? Would I pass the test of the Egyptian Gods of receiving and giving joy?

Perhaps, in the end, none of it matters. One life may be less significant than a grain of sand in the desert. Yet, it is also true that a single life can make all the difference in the world. One person can influence the lives of others, both present and in the future. One person can change the world. You only need to think of men like Thomas Edison, Albert Einstein, Martin Luther King, and Charles Darwin. Or, women like Marie Curie, Helen Keller, Rosa Parks, Anne Frank and Eva Peron.

It was only when I discovered the Ethos that I became truly mindful of how I spent my time or what my life could mean. Until that time I had been surviving, just trying to get by like everyone else. I'd never really given much thought to the things that mattered to me, or the things that mattered to the people around me. I had been living on autopilot, going through the motions, stuck on a soulless loop of work, TV, and sleep. It was only after finding the ethos that I began consciously, mindfully, to build a life.

Through the ethos I came to realise that all any of us can hope for is to make the most of the time and the resources we're given. We can't change the hand we're dealt, but we can play those cards to the best of our ability and, with a bit of luck, when our time comes to leave, the places we lived and the people we met will be a little better, a little happier, than they were when we found them. That is the very least, and perhaps the most, to which any of us can aspire.

Had I passed earlier in life, my organs might have found new bodies to inhabit. I always carried an organ donor card with me with that in mind. If I had died in an accident and my eyes had been able to give sight to the blind, or my kidneys had been able to relieve the suffering of someone with kidney disease, that would have made me happy. But there is little use for anything in my body. So, I elected to be cremated.

The following month, both my son and my daughter flew over to Sun Park with their spouses and children to fulfil my last wish. Greg and Christina had notified the community, and when my family arrived, many of my friends were there to greet them.

The crowd congregated in the north gardens in front of a fig tree, my final resting place. My son, James, read from one of my favourite poems, written by the famous Native American, Chief Seattle:

This we know. The earth does not belong to us, we belong to earth.

This we know. All things are connected like the blood which unites one family.

All things are connected.

My daughter then read the words written by American Poet, Walt Whitman:

We were together. I forget the rest.

For me, those pieces of prose capture the very essence of the ethos. We remember the times we spent together, everything else fades. Like the Chinese man in the fable, we travel through life hoping to arrive at a place that fills us with joy and happiness, only to discover that neither joy nor happiness reside in a place, even a place called 'Sun Park'. True joy and happiness happen throughout our journey in Life, emerging from the moments we spend together, when we feel connected.

The ancient Egyptians believed that everyone has two deaths, the first when their heart stops beating and the second when they no longer exist in anyone's memory.

This is the message echoed in the ethos too: make yours a memorable journey, for yourself and for others, because life is better, richer, happier and more fulfilled when shared. And, long after your body has turned to dust, you'll live on in people's memories. Everything else is forgotten.

If you should find your way to Sun Park, I know that you'll receive a warm welcome from the community. You may arrive, like I did, expecting a holiday, perhaps a rest, but if you embrace the people you meet, you'll experience something much more precious and meaningful...an ethos that can change your life.

Whilst you are there, if you take the time to walk around the gardens, amid the palm trees, the cacti and aloe plants, and the lavender flowers, you'll find me. There is a fig tree shading a wooden bench. Feel free to take a seat. If you close your eyes and listen carefully, you may hear the sound of the ethos in the air... all things are connected.

~

ACKNOWLEDGEMENTS

The Ethos is inspired by the community at The Sun Park Village resort on the island of Lanzarote. I would like to thank every member and guest, even those I didn't meet because whilst Sun Park touches the lives of everyone who visits, every visitor - however, short or long their stay - becomes part of the community. To name everyone I met and spoke with during my visits would fill the pages of this book, and more. They all gave generously of their time and openly shared their stories. I am indebted to them all.

I must give special thanks to Gil Summers and his partner, Patricia Dominguez. The ethos is largely the result of their shared vision. Certainly, without them and their unwavering dedication to their vision and their courage and determination to see it through, neither the Sun Park resort nor the community or the ethos that came from it, would exist today.

ABOUT THE AUTHOR

Adam J Jackson originally qualified and worked as a solicitor in the mid-1980's before re-training in Natural Therapies. He went on to become a monthly columnist for the Nursing Times and Health Guardian, specialising in reviewing the latest research in natural health sciences, complementary medicines and drug-free therapies.

Adam quickly became a leading proponent in his field. In 2001, he appeared on behalf of the British Complementary Medical Association before the House of Lords Select Committee reviewing Alternative & Complementary Therapies in the UK. He has appeared on national television in the UK and North America, and numerous articles of his have been published in national magazines.

Adam is the author of ten books in the mind, body and spirit and business/personal development niches. These include **'The Secrets of Abundant Health, Wealth, Love & Happiness'** series which has been translated and published in 27 languages around the world. Adam's most recent book, **'The Flipside: Finding the hidden opportunities in life'** is currently available in 17 languages.

CONNECT WITH ADAM!

Connect with Adam and subscribe to his V.I.P. list to receive news, updates and exclusive promotions:

To join the V.I.P. club, visit:
http://adamjjackson.com/vip-club/

WEB
http://adamjjackson.com

TWITTER
https://twitter.com/adamjjackson

FACEBOOK
https://facebook.com/adamjohnjackson

If you enjoyed this book, please consider submitting a review on Amazon.com – thank you!

OTHER BOOKS BY ADAM J JACKSON

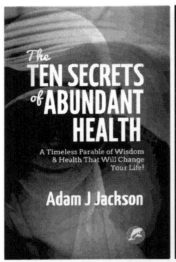
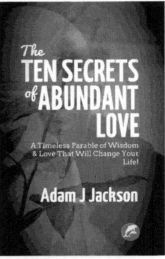
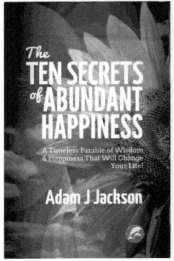
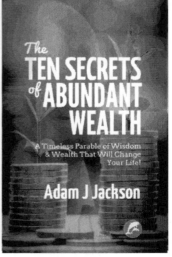

'*The Flipside* shows you that every cloud can have a silver lining. Brilliant'

THE
FLIPSIDE

Finding the hidden opportunities in life

Adam J Jackson

'This is an inspiring, really energising book. It is just the sort of thing you need when you have watched too many news broadcasts about how the world is going to the dogs...This is an empowering book. Read it first before you give it to that friend who really needs it.'

The Times - South Africa - 25th April 2009

'We are inspired by Adam J Jackson's writings in his book "The Flipside" which is based upon a simple and inspiring idea that "every problem or obstacle in our lives however big or small contains an equivalent or greater benefit or opportunity.'

Health budget speech tabled by Limpopo MEC for Health and Social Development, Mrs Miriam Segabutla. 18 June 2009. Department of Health and Social Development, **Limpopo Provincial Government**

'Life-affirming stories guaranteed to make us change the way we look at adversity'
Publishers Weekly

'An entertaining and relevant read when so many people are facing financial and emotional traumas.'
News of The World

Printed in Great Britain
by Amazon